Anna

A LIFE OF FAITH AND COURAGE

TRAVIS SHORT

Best Wishes

[signature]

Publish Authority

Anna: A Life of Faith and Courage

ISBN 978-1-954000-46-9 (Paperback)
ISBN 978-1-954000-47-6 (eBook)

Published 2023 by Publish Authority,
300 Colonial Center Parkway, Suite 100
Roswell, GA USA
PublishAuthority.com

Printed in the United States of America

To Anna, whose true story is embodied in this fictional account of her life, and to my brother, James, who befriended her and brought her remarkable story to my attention.

Foreword

The story of Anna might never have been told if not for the recognition by her children of her unique qualities, goodness, and faith. The account of her life, much of it written in her own words, tells of a battered and sickly child who survived against inconceivable odds to find an unshakeable belief that our lives are in the hands of an almighty creator. Her words form the basis for the account you are about to read. Anna's story should be a source of inspiration and encouragement regardless of your philosophical or religious beliefs.

Throughout history, people have overcome overwhelming odds to accomplish great goals. None of their stories are more compelling than that of Elie Wiesel, a Holocaust survivor who lost his mother and sister at Auschwitz and his father at Buchenwald. He and his family were captured by the Germans when Elie was seventeen. He survived the next eighteen months in German concentration camps by adapting a will to live under the direst circumstances when those around him gave up. He explained his survival in his book titled *Night,* in which he declared that we cannot always determine our circumstances, but we can control how we think and react to them. His will to survive kept him alive until he was liberated at the end of World War II, the only surviving member of his family. He went on to write several books and to reveal to the world the horrors heaped upon the Jewish people of Europe.

Anna Marie Gamble was not a prisoner of the concentration camps, but she *was* a prisoner of circumstances into which she was born. She survived by adopting the attitude later voiced by Elie Wiesel. By doing so, she changed her circumstances. When she discovered a profound belief in God and the salvation of Jesus Christ, she was able to endure the cruel influences surrounding her. Despised by her mother, whom she saw only infrequently, and mistreated by an alcoholic father, she prospered in her faith.

We have no way of knowing why certain people emerge from improbable beginnings, but we know they do. I am reminded of a poem titled "Born Without a Chance," written in 1809 by Edmund Vance Cook, describing the birth of Abraham Lincoln, who, despite his beginnings, went on to become the sixteenth president and ended slavery in America. Like Lincoln, Anna was born with little chance of survival and certainly not much probability of achieving any recognizable success. However, she did succeed. And whatever she accomplished, she attributed to her strong faith, which this story *Anna* portrays.

Preface

Anna Marie Gamble was ninety-six when I met her, nearly eight years ago, in the Westwood Convalescent Center. I had just admitted my wife, Mary, who was suffering from Alzheimer's. Anna was a diminutive woman, scarcely five feet tall, with dark penetrating eyes, full of wisdom and still full of life. She stood before a large goldfish aquarium, her face almost touching the glass. Her hands grasped the handles of a push walker as she leaned closer to see the fish. I must have startled her as I approached because she turned to look at me suddenly, apparently surprised at my encroachment on her serenity.

"Who are you?" she asked, looking up into my face.

"James Morris," I replied, "and may I ask your name?"

"Anna," she said, "Anna."

She returned her attention to the aquarium. "Do you think there are fish in Heaven?"

"Probably," I said, "but I have never thought much about it."

"I hope so. But I will know before long because I am going to Heaven soon." She grasped her walker and backed away from the goldfish.

"I hope not," I said, "at least not before I get to know you better."

She began pushing her walker to the main corridor leading to the patients' rooms. When we reached room 204, she stopped and peered in. "This is where I live."

On the door were the names of two patients; the bottom name was *Anna Marie Gamble.*

"Where is your room?" she asked.

"Oh, I don't live here. It's my wife, Mary. She is in room 232."

"Give her my love." Anna turned into her room. She sat in a chair near her bed. I watched for a moment as she took a harmonica from her pocket and began to play "It Is Well with My Soul."

The strains of the music followed me to Mary's room, where the attendants were completing the chores to get her settled into her new surroundings. Through a mixture of emotions, I approached Mary's bed, took her into my arms, and held her close to me for several minutes. Somehow, I knew my encounter with Anna was preordained and that her presence would prove to be a blessing for Mary and me.

In the next few days, I would encounter Anna in the hallways, at the noon and evening meals, or in an assembly area where the patients went through mild exercises, playing games or listening to readings by one of the attendants. During most of those encounters, we carried on meaningful conversations. Still, there were times when she slipped into cognitive lapses, confusing the past with the present, detailing information about her husband, George, and her four children, the youngest being sixty-one, four years younger than I. I usually heard a rendition of "Amazing Grace" or "Nothing but the Blood of Jesus" when I passed her room. She followed each song with a burst of "Pop Goes the Weasel." It always brought a smile to my face.

Before the month was out, I became Anna's protector by default. She had no visitors on a regular basis, whereas I spent most of each day with my wife, assisting her with meals and making certain she had the attention from attendants as required. I met Anna's youngest daughter, Marie, when she visited the facility during Mary's second month of residency. Anna was aware of Marie's impending visit and told me about it every day until her daughter arrived.

"I have family coming to see me soon."

"That's nice. Who is it?"

"Marie, my youngest child. She is named after me."

"That will be wonderful, Anna. I hope I get to meet her."

"You will," she said. "Her husband is coming too. He is a pastor. His name is Frank. I hope they recognize me. It has been so long since I've seen them."

"I wouldn't worry if I were you. You would be hard to forget."

She smiled. "Thank you, dear. Just remember to eat your vegetables."

I subdued a laugh but assured her with the utmost respect
that I would do as I was told.

For the remainder of the month, I encountered Anna in the
hallways at least once daily. She faithfully made her sojourn to
the goldfish aquarium, spent several minutes talking to the fish
then returned to her room. Soon, the music of her harmonica
could be heard in all the intersecting hallways. It was as though
she gained inspiration from her visits to the aquarium. I would
stand in the doorway of Mary's room so I could hear Anna's
accomplished playing. Many of the songs I recalled from my
childhood when my siblings and I attended church and Sunday
School with our mother. It was during those moments when
Anna played that I gained such fondness for her, and I resolved
to watch over her just as I did for Mary. The attendants were
not as thorough as they should be because of limited staffing
and high personnel turnover. I am certain some of the staff
resented my prodding, but I was determined to see that both
Mary and Anna were adequately cared for.

The month passed with its usual routine, with me arriving
at the center at about ten a.m. to make sure Mary was taken
out of bed, washed, and dressed. That did not always happen,
and I was not hesitant to make known my disappointment to
her attendant for the day and the nurse on duty at the front
desk. After caring for Mary, I would walk sixty feet to Anna's
room to ensure she received the same care. I usually brought
with me a chocolate candy bar, which Anna ate with glee.
Perhaps she was compensating for all the candy and treats she

had not been privileged to have as a child. I indulged myself with the pleasure of watching her devour the candy bars each day, giving no consideration to any diet restrictions she might need to observe. It was my opinion that, at ninety-six, she should be able to enjoy any pleasure she wished.

One morning I visited her room, a Snickers bar in hand. She was gone when I arrived, but I knew where to find her. I walked in the direction of the aquarium and met Anna on her way back to her room.

"Where is your walker, Anna?"

"What's that?" She looked perplexed.

"You know what that is," I said, "and you aren't supposed to leave your room without your walker. You might fall."

"How old are you?"

"Old enough to know you need your walker."

"Well, young man, when you get to be my age, you can tell me what to do."

I laughed. "I know, but where is your walker?"

"I think I left it with the fish. Do you want to go with me to get it?"

"No. I will take you back to your room, then go find the walker for you."

"You are a nice man," she said. "But I don't need any help finding my room. My name is on the door."

"I know," I said, "but you don't mind if I walk with you, do you?"

"If you don't get too pushy."

I suppressed a smile and said to myself, *No wonder you have lived to such a nice old age.*

Another month had almost passed, and Anna still had not had visitors. I wondered if her daughter was imaginary, someone she conjured in one of the moments when she seemed to depart from lucidity. But my doubts were removed one Saturday morning when I heard beautiful gospel singing coming from Anna's room. The door was ajar and partially open, permitting me to see into the room. I stood outside and listened along with several patients attracted by the beautiful singing.

When the duet finished "Nearer My God to Thee." I knocked gently on the door.

Anna looked up and pointed in my direction. "This is Marie, my daughter," she said, "She came to visit me. She knew me right away."

I stepped inside the room and introduced myself, then said to Anna, "I told you that you would be hard to forget, didn't I?"

She laughed. "She's my baby daughter, you know."

"Yes, you told me. I am so happy to meet her, finally."

Marie was attractive and modestly dressed. She was petite but still three or four inches taller than her mother. I soon gathered that she was as steeped in religiosity as Anna was. A Bible and hymn book lay on the bed near where Marie sat. Next to the Bible was a looseleaf binder containing a hundred or so pages. On the front cover was the name *Anna Marie Gamble*. My eyes were fixed on the binder because I could not help but wonder what was contained between its covers. Marie anticipated my curiosity. "That book contains my mother's history as she recalled it at age eighty-four."

"I would love to read it," I said. "She is such an interesting woman."

"It is very personal, very revealing."

"I understand," I said.

I explained to Marie my wife's condition and how I visited each day and looked after Anna just as I did Mary. "I have come to love this lady. I hope I can be half as vigorous if I live to be her age."

"Me too," Marie said through laughter. "My mother is a wonder and has been all her life, even as a child."

I left the room and went back to check on Mary. Sounds of "Let Us Have a Little Talk with Jesus" followed me down the corridor.

That afternoon, I pushed Mary's wheelchair outside, near the front entrance, to enjoy the early fall weather. A few minutes later, Marie came out of the facility, accompanied by her husband, Frank. She made an introduction, explaining that he was a pastor for hospice and was visiting patients in the different wings of the convalescent center. We spoke for a few minutes before they walked to the parking lot. As I watched after them, Marie turned back and began walking in our direction. She held up her mother's book for me to see. I got up from the bench and met her. She handed the binder to me. "I think Mother would want you to have this."

As I drove home, the document lay on the seat beside me. After dinner, I sat in my recliner before the television set but did not turn it on. My mind was on the book that lay on the arm of the chair. I read the name *Anna Marie Gamble*. Somehow it seemed inappropriate for me to read the privileged account of her life even though the book had been given to me for that purpose. The sounds of her gospel songs filled my head. I smiled as I envisioned her eating a chocolate candy bar.

"Go ahead and read," her voice seemed to coax me.

Filled with misgivings, I could no longer resist. I wanted to know more about the lady I had come to admire and protect. I opened the binder and began to read.

Chapter One

BEFORE I BEGIN

I cannot begin this account before giving thanks to my gracious and blessed Heavenly Father who understands the hearts and lives and needs of his children. I give Him praise for the life about which I now begin to write.

I was given a blank book, as a gift, by my daughter and her husband for Christmas in 2001. They requested that before I leave this planet for my Heavenly home, I write about events of my journey through life on earth. I have endured for eighty-four years, some in bliss, some in desperation, and I shall write about them all. I am thankful for all the years God has given me. I trust He believes I have used them wisely and in His service.

I was born on March 12, 1918, the seventh, born into a family of ten children. Three of my siblings passed away before my birth, and one when I was the age of four, so I will meet them for the first time in Heaven.

As I write this, only two of my siblings are still alive. I am the only one able to enjoy all of God's blessings; a loving family, good friends, memories of a good husband, and the ability to serve the Lord. For all that He has given me, it is my pleasure to pass on His blessings to others. Nothing gives me greater satisfaction than to be a comforter when God lets me see the need. Nothing makes me happier than when I can bring encouragement to others because I remember how much it meant to me when others encouraged me. I meet my Savior, my chief encourager, when I am encouraging others. My sight is failing, but I trust that He will grant me the ability to see well enough to write this record of my life. I trust God for whatever lies ahead for me. As I continue my journey here on earth, I am looking to Him, who is omnipresent, omniscient, and omnipotent, for guidance and salvation. This account is for His glory and is told as truthfully as my memory will allow me to recall.

Chapter Two

HONOR THY FATHER AND THY MOTHER

I have very few fond memories of my mother. I have few of my father as well except for his love of music, which he passed on to all of us. As far back as I can remember, my family never owned a home and we were constantly moving, sometimes into rundown shacks or, at best, apartments or houses minimally suited for habitation by humans. Our mother was seldom home. Sometimes she was away for months or even a year or more without my father knowing where she was living or hearing from her. She returned home when she had no place else to go. We children viewed her as a fairy godmother who came into our lives bearing gifts but leaving our lives in more disarray. All of us were happy to see her go.

As I gained an understanding of the Word of God, I grew troubled by the difficulty I experienced in my early life, attempting to abide by the commandment in Exodus 20:12, "Honor Thy father and Thy mother so that thou may live long in the land thy Lord has given thee." Thankfully, with age, came wisdom. As I matured and found God, I learned forgiveness, and with forgiveness, came honor for my parents. None of us is perfect, not I and not my mother and father. Even in their disconnected and confused lives they professed a belief in God. In their moments of relative tranquility, they told us of the redemption of sins through Jesus Christ. At that time, I had no understanding of the salvation offered by an acceptance of Him. The turmoil we children witnessed almost daily when my parents were together made me doubt that there was a God or that Jesus Christ existed. My parents gave me very little reason to honor them but when I became a Christian, I found myself more able to forgive them and show them honor.

My father was a hard-working man. He did odd jobs wherever he could find them and sharecropped much of his life. He also made money playing his accordion for dances and county fairs. When I was growing up there was never a time that my father did not have to struggle to keep us all fed. I think my mother was ashamed of the way we had to live, and I assumed that was her main reason for leaving us for such long periods of time.

I believe my father loved my mother until the day he died, and perhaps there was a time when my mother was in love with him. But by the time I was born, her love had changed to hate. During her infrequent visits, she and my father argued continually. He could not conceal his jealousy and often accused my mother of unseemly conduct, which mother denied vehemently. We children dared not take sides in their altercations and we cowered in a corner or in another room.

One of my first memories as a four-year-old was of an

argument between them that turned violent. As they hurled accusations at each other, their voices rising in intensity, I held my three-year-old brother, Horton, close to me under the kitchen table. Although we didn't understand his condition at the time, Horton was mentally disabled. Father loved him more than any of his other children and gave me the responsibility of keeping him safe, even from my father's own volatile temper.

It was late in the summer, just after my fourth birthday. Mother returned home and stayed longer than usual. For some reason she did not love me and concocted reasons for punishing me for no reason. Although she appeared not to love Horton as my father and I did, she often accused me of neglecting him. I was afraid of her and I found reasons to stay close to my father when she was home. However, there were times my father would agree with my mother and punish me as well. My savior at that time was my older sister, Margie, who was fourteen when I was four. She often came to my rescue and chided my father or mother for mistreating me.

My father was a wonderful musician and could play almost any instrument at his disposal. He loved his accordion, which he often played at church service and most weekends for local dances. My mother was experiencing a difficult pregnancy with my youngest sibling, Althea, and was unusually irritable. As my father prepared to leave for the evening to play at the community center, Mother expressed her displeasure at being left at home. My father, who always considered himself alone, took umbrage at my mother's criticism.

"You have a lot of nerve, Della. You stay away for weeks or months leaving me here to fend for myself and the children.

Now, you don't want to be left alone with them. It wouldn't harm you to get to know your own children. Besides, Margie will be here if you need anything while I'm gone."

My mother bristled at father's comments. At first, she just glowered, but when she saw her anger would not change my father's intention to go to the dance and take all the children but me and Horton, she blurted out her rage. She pointed at me. "You are leaving me here with these little imps. I'm pregnant and could deliver at any minute."

I pulled Horton close to me and shivered as I crawled under the kitchen table.

Father threw the accordion strap across his shoulder and took hold of the doorknob.

"It doesn't matter that you may need to go for a midwife at any minute." She put both hands on her protruding stomach. "Can't you see I am pregnant?"

"I know you're pregnant, but by who?" My father screamed at my mother, no more than six inches from her ear.

She clawed down the sides of his face.

My father dropped the accordion to his feet and wiped his hands down his cheeks. There was a hurt in his eyes I had never seen before as he looked at his bloody hands. He stood in silence for a few moments then slowly raised his hand and slapped my mother across her face. She fell to the floor.

As mother got to her knees, she looked up at my father. "You will live to regret this, Daniel Duvall."

My father opened the door and walked out to where the horse and buggy awaited with my sixteen-year-old brother, Jerome, at the reins. My sister, Margie, closed the door behind him then offered mother her hand. She slapped the hand away, defiantly pulled a chair from the table and sat. Her body began to shake as tears flowed.

"I will get even," she said. "You children just wait and see."

I held Horton close, frozen in fear near my mother's feet.

Chapter Three

THE PLOT

Althea was born three weeks later. My Aunt Cora came to live with us a few days before the birth and acted as a midwife. While she and Mother planned for the delivery of the baby, I often heard them talking softly from inside Mother's bedroom. The hatred for Father that I overheard frightened me.

"I swear I would kill him if I could get away with it," my mother's voice was almost in a whisper.

"There are ways," Aunt Cora said.

"I could get a gun and claim he tried to kill me."

Mother seemed to find humor in her idea and chuckled. I could imagine her hand over her mouth to conceal her laugh.

Aunt Cora's voice was lowered as she responded. "No, honey, you wouldn't have to do anything so obvious or violent; there's poison."

"Poison?"

"Yes, arsenic," Aunt Cora said, "and it would be hard to

prove. He might go in his sleep, and that would be the end of it."

"Where would I get arsenic?"

"I know someone. I'll get it for you."

I wanted to run to my father and tell him what I had heard, but I was afraid he would mention it to my mother, and she would beat me the first time we were alone. So, I decided to tell Margie what I had heard. She told me not to worry, that she would look out for my father so that no harm would come to him.

As the day approached for the new baby to be born, we all waited with anticipation. Because Horton was mentally impaired, I hoped my new sibling would be a boy that perhaps my father would love as much as he did Horton. Mother and Margie wanted a girl. But I was just as pleased as they were when our baby girl was born.

My father was working in the field and didn't come home until two hours after Althea arrived. If he still had misgivings about the source of Mother's pregnancy, he never let them show. He went straight to Mother's bedside and picked up the baby.

"It's a girl," Aunt Cora said, "She has your features, Daniel."

Father held the baby away from him to examine her face. "Her eyes aren't open. Is something wrong?"

"We don't know," Aunt Cora said, "Maybe they will be open by tomorrow morning. We will just have to wait and see."

Mother was distraught and turned her face to the wall. She sobbed quietly as father laid Althea on the bed close to her.

We all left the room, hoping mother and Althea would

sleep, but we heard the baby crying for a long time after we were in bed.

Next morning, Mother was up and about early. Aunt Cora had packed her few clothes, which were in a small satchel by the door. Jerome waited outside with the horse and buggy, ready to drive her home, about five miles away. My mother and her sister held each other and whispered just before Aunt Cora opened the door to leave.

I wondered if they were whispering about killing Papa.

Another week passed and Althea had not yet opened her eyes. She cried incessantly. When Dad returned home from the field that evening, Mother was gone. We had no idea how long she would be away. Margie was left to care for the new baby and her five other siblings. We later heard Mother was running a boarding house in Scranton.

The next day, Dad drove his horse and buggy to the nearest village where there was a doctor. He came home with formula and eyedrops for Althea.

Margie was devoted to our baby sister and administered drops twice each day. A month later, Althea opened her eyes. We all shouted, "Praise the Lord." Even though I had no idea what that meant, I loved the exuberance and joined in with my tiny voice shouting at the top of my lungs, "Praise the Lord, praise the Lord, praise the Lord."

Dad placed his hand gently on my head. "Yes, honey, praise the Lord, for he is good."

I remember how much I loved my father at that moment and hoped no harm would come to him.

❄

My dad's moods were difficult to anticipate, especially when Mother was away from home for long periods. He eagerly accepted every opportunity to earn a little money to buy food or pay our rent. Sometimes, he came home in a jovial mood, but often he did not allow us children to be in the same room with him. When he was in such a mood, he often found solitude in playing his accordion. He loved gospel tunes, especially the song "This Train is Bound for Glory."

The boardinghouse that Mother ran in Scranton was only twenty miles from our home on Mr. Sherman's farm. She came to see us more frequently than usual but spent only two or three days on each visit. While my dad was out working in the field or doing odd jobs in town, Mother would do her utmost to turn us all against our father. She openly talked of her plans for all of us after his death. By the time she returned to Scranton, we younger children were convinced that Dad was a demon out to harm all of us. I don't believe Margie or my two older brothers, Ralph and Jerome, ever believed Dad was evil. Rather, they were suspicious of my mother's motives, especially when she and Aunt Cora were together at our house.

During one of Mother's visits, she stayed for about a week and was uncharacteristically sweet to my father. She slept in his bed and each morning made breakfast of biscuits and gravy for all of us. I had never seen my father happier, and having the two of them together, showing tenderness for each other, made all of us children incredibly happy.

The following Saturday evening, my dad took all of us to a community dance where he played the accordion. Mother and Margie stayed home to care for Horton and Althea. When we returned, Mother told my dad to sit while she removed his boots. After this loving gesture, she brought a cup of coffee to him, kissed his forehead, and said, "I love you, Daniel."

"And I love you, Della." Tears filled my father's eyes.

I was not yet five years old, but a sense of terror rushed through me. I wanted to scream, "Don't drink that, Papa."

I looked at Margie. She was smiling, happy that our parents were sharing their love for each other with all their children. Her smile gave me comfort.

The next morning, Mother was gone before anyone else was awake.

Chapter Four

DEATH IN THE FAMILY

The screams coming from my father's room were loud enough to wake all of us. I heard Margie rushing through the house to see what was happening. A few minutes later, Ralph and Jerome were by his bedside. Jerome held a bucket to catch Papa's vomit. I sat quietly by the door, listening to the commotion and wondering what had made my father so ill. It occurred to me that the coffee my mother served him the night before was poisoned, but I could not believe she was actually that evil. However, I think Margie knew right away what our mother was capable of doing.

"I need to go to the outhouse," Papa grunted. "My stomach is killing me."

"No," Ralph said, "I'll bring the pot to you."

Margie understood that something terrible had happened to our father. She took charge of the situation and calmly directed my brothers.

"Jerome, get the horse and buggy ready to take daddy to

the doctor. You may have to take him to Scranton if Doctor Williamson is not in his office."

Doctor Williamson had an office about ten miles from our house. He was the one who prescribed eye drops for Althea, but he was often away from his practice making house calls.

Jerome slipped on his last boot and then ran out the door to the barn.

Ralph attempted to help our father sit, but he was paralyzed and unable to move his legs, and then shortly, Papa lapsed into unconsciousness.

Margie dropped to her knees and prayed, asking God to save our father and forgive our mother. After a moment, she seemed to gain strength not evident in most fourteen-year-olds. She walked to the front door and called out to Jerome, "Papa can't move. Go find Doctor Williamson and bring him back here."

We all waited, mostly without talking, for Jerome to return. It seemed like eternity but, as I recall, it was about three hours later when we heard the horse and buggy stop outside our door. With a black satchel at his side, Dr. Williamson, ran into the house and up the stairs. Margie pulled a chair alongside the bed for the doctor to sit. He spoke Papa's name, but he was not responsive.

Dr. Williamson put a stethoscope on Papa's chest. "Can you hear me, Mr. Duvall?"

Father flickered his hand but was unable to speak.

The doctor turned to Margie. "What has he eaten lately?"

"Supper last night, boiled potatoes and dandelion greens," she responded, then after a moment, added, "and he drank a cup of coffee."

"Perhaps, there was something in the dandelions," the doctor said. "Did everyone else eat them?"

"Yes," Margie responded, "but they were washed clean before we cooked them."

The doctor put his stethoscope on Papa's chest again and listened. He then asked Jerome and Ralph to leave the room. We sat close to the closed door listening to the muffled sounds of conversation between Margie and Doctor Williamson but understood only an occasional word or two. After several minutes he emerged, carrying his satchel. He never spoke as Jerome followed him down the stairs and out the door to the waiting horse and buggy. Ralph followed to accompany him on his trip to take Doctor Williamson back to his office. It would be three more hours before our brothers returned.

When Margie came from our father's room, she wiped away tears.

"What's wrong with Papa?" my eight-year-old sister, Loretta, asked.

"He's very sick," she said. "You children be good. I have things to do."

With our mother gone, and Father debilitated with some unknown malady, she was the head of our household. That evening, after Ralph and Jerome returned, she read the Twenty-Third Psalm from the Bible, it was the first time I ever heard it.

"We must all pray for Papa; pray that God does not take him away from us now when we need him so badly. And pray for Mother; she needs our prayers too."

Word reached Mother that our father was dying. Two weeks later, she returned home to see for herself. I can only imagine her disappointment when she saw that Papa was improving. He had some feeling in his arms and legs and was able to sit upright on the edge of the bed. Margie suggested that he try to walk, but he was unable to stand on his feet without terrible pain. His toes turned under, and he was unable to get his boots on. The condition stayed with him for the remainder of his life.

We had no idea how long Mom planned to stay with us, but she presumed to take charge of things again, and we settled in with her running the household and preparing meals. As I think about that period, I recall that Margie stayed close to Mother, especially when she prepared Papa's meals, which Margie always fed him. One evening, Mother took a tray of food to my father. She bent to place the tray on the chair near his bed.

My father said, "You'll have to feed me. I can't feed myself."

She slammed the tray of food down on the chair. "Then starve." She said, cursing him as she walked downstairs,

Papa held a fork and attempted to feed himself, but he was unable to grasp the fork properly, dropping food onto his bed and the floor.

Margie heard Mother's cursing and realized something was wrong. She ran up the stairs and offered to feed Papa.

"Never mind," he said. "I'm no longer hungry. Jerome can feed me tonight when he comes home."

Aunt Cora came the next day. She and Mother left together that evening. Mother never told us where she was going or how long she might be gone. No one asked because we all knew she probably had no idea and wouldn't have told us if she had known.

Margie could play all the musical instruments that Papa played. About three weeks after his narrow escape from death, she brought the accordion to his bedroom and played his favorite tune; "This Train is Bound for Glory." All of us children ran to Papa's room, thinking that he was playing his accordion. Although it was Margie making the music, we all rejoiced to see Papa patting his foot and clapping his hands. The following week he put the strap across his shoulder and played "Amazing Grace." I have come to believe that it was never before or since played with such thanksgiving.

Two days later, Papa made his way downstairs, carrying the accordion. We were all sitting around the table, waiting to hear him play. Althea, Horton, and Loretta were all near Papa's feet under the table when Loretta began to cry.

Margie pulled back her chair and leaned down. "What's wrong, honey?

"Something's wrong with Horton."

Margie got onto her hands and knees and pulled Horton to her.

"He isn't breathing!"

She lowered her face over his and began blowing air into his lungs, but Horton didn't respond. Margie lifted him from the floor and held him out for Papa to see.

"This baby is dead," she said. "He has gone to be with our Lord."

Papa's hands began to shake. He called out my little brother's name. "Horton! Horton!"

Margie placed our brother's lifeless body on her chair and checked his tiny wrist for a pulse.

"He's gone, Father. There's nothing we can do."

Papa removed the accordion straps from his shoulders. He flung the instrument with all his might against the wall. The accordion whined like a dying kitten as it slowly closed.

We buried Horton the next day in a wood casket that Jerome made.

Chapter Five

THE VISION

Under an oak tree in Mr. Sherman's family cemetery, my baby brother's funeral was a sad occasion. I had never before heard a sermon about someone like Horton being in Heaven when I could see his pale face right there in front of me. I pondered the words of Reverend Cantrell for several days after my brothers helped shovel dirt over the wood coffin. I wondered if Horton could really run and play and be a normal boy, just as the preacher had said. If that was true, I thought Horton may be better off than I was, still living down here on earth, often hungry, afraid of my mother's cruelty when she was home, and afraid of my father's unpredictable temper.

The funeral was especially difficult for my father, who loved Horton so much. Papa was unable to stand for long periods. He sat close to the little wood casket with his hand pressed against its side. Occasionally, I heard him sob, but he mostly held his head high and looked at the box holding his dearest child. I am sure he wondered why Mother did not come to the funeral after Jerome drove the buggy all the way to Scranton to tell her of Horton's death.

Papa was unable to perform any meaningful jobs for at least two months because he had difficulty standing with his turned-down toes. His accordion was unplayable for several days while Jerome and Ralph worked to put everything back together. During these times, we had little money and not much to feed a family of seven. Mr. Sherman informed Papa that we must move out of his old house if rent could not be paid. So, Margie and my two brothers went from neighbor to neighbor asking for help but never received enough to pay even part of the rent, which was two months overdue. Of course, there was no prospect of paying rent the next month either.

Throughout my life, often when I least expected it, God came to my rescue. Because Papa was well known in our community, he was contacted by someone who told him of a kind Christian lady by the name of Nora Walker. She had been a widow for two years. When she heard of our situation, she sent her brother to invite us to move in with her. By then, Papa was partially recovered. His accordion was repaired, and he was able to play at dances again. Because he had trouble standing for very long, he frequently played while sitting down. When he was not working, he was traveling about our county looking for an apartment where we could have a home of our own, and he could be close to the new work he had found.

While Papa was gone, Mrs. Walker looked after me and my sister Althea. Loretta was big enough to help her, but Althea was a fussy child and required near-constant attention. She appeared to be very bright but had an uncontrollable tendency to rock back and forth as she sat. So, we dared not leave her alone for more than a few minutes.

My sister, Margie, was the nearest thing to a mother I ever had. She kept me as close to her as possible, even when she was helping Mrs. Walker do chores. Although we never spoke of it, I am sure she realized my mother did not love me or perhaps even like me for some reason. When Margie began dating Anthony, I was jealous of him, afraid I would lose her if she ever married him. Anthony was a large man who worked for Mr. Sherman. He was much older than Margie and was always unkempt. A scraggly beard made him appear very ominous.

I always slept with Margie and snuggled close to her, fearing something would happen to me if I got too far away. One evening when we were in bed, I was having a difficult time getting to sleep. I could hear Margie's deep breathing next to me and knew she was sleeping. Suddenly, a tall, dark figure appeared at the foot of our bed. I wanted to scream but did not wish to startle everyone else in the house. The figure just stood there, his bulging eyes looking directly at me. He lifted a finger and pointed.

"You are a troublemaker," the figure said. A flash of light gave me a brief look at a dark, angry face.

"Why?" I asked in a voice so faint I barely heard myself speak.

"Because your sister does not want to leave you. Why don't you run away?"

I became so frightened, but I was afraid to speak. At five years old where would I go? I wanted to ask Margie if she wanted to leave me with Papa and marry Anthony, but I stayed silent and pulled the covers over my face. I squinted to see what the figure was doing next, but it just stood there. Suddenly, I heard a loud sound. It was as if someone was dragging a large chain across the floor. I thought the chains were surely meant for me, that maybe it should have been me who died and not Horton.

As I lay in bed, afraid to make a noise, I could faintly hear Papa playing the accordion downstairs. Suddenly, he stopped playing.

"What's all that noise up there?"

I pulled the cover from my face and looked toward the foot of the bed. The figure slunk away, still pulling the chain behind it.

Papa called again, "What is that noise upstairs?"

I held my breath and waited for him to call again.

Margie sat up and went to the door. "What noise, Papa?"

Papa said nothing more.

Margie came back to bed and held me close. "You're shivering, baby. What's wrong?"

"Nothing," I said, clinging to her. "I love you so much, Margie."

She was still holding me when I fell asleep safe in her arms.

I've pondered this for eighty years and wish I had told her about my vision. It might have saved both of us from many sorrows.

To my horror, soon after that, Margie informed Papa that she and Anthony were going to be married and that she would take me with her. I wanted to be with Margie, but I did not want her to marry Anthony. Her life at home had been one of drudgery, with responsibilities for all of us from the time she was nine years old, responsibilities that should have been my mother's. I wanted to go with Margie but had a lingering fear of Anthony.

Two weeks later, Papa drove with Margie and Anthony to Scranton, where they were married by the county judge. They returned to our house, and that night, Anthony slept with Margie in our bed. As I lay beside Loretta that night, I could envision Anthony's face staring at me from the foot of the bed. I knew then that he was the dark figure in my vision.

B y the grace of God, Papa was able to find a large home in Union Dale, Pennsylvania. It was far away from his new work but enabled us to leave Mrs. Walker's kind hospitality. The house provided us with plenty of room but was old and rundown. There was an extra bedroom that allowed Margie and Anthony privacy. It meant that I would spend less and less time with her. That made me hate Anthony even more. I hoped that Papa would find us an apartment in Scranton, close to his job. Maybe then we would leave Anthony behind because he worked on Mr. Sherman's farm, which was twenty miles from Scranton.

Everyone else in my family appeared to be very happy to have Anthony living in our house. I admit it was beneficial because he helped pay the bills for about two months. God knows we needed all the help we could get because of Papa's inability to work for so long. I stayed as far away from Anthony as I could because I was unable to get the image of him standing at the foot of my bed out of my mind. Also, he was gruff with Margie, ordering her about as if she were a child. Although I wanted to be with Margie, I had a fear about living with her and Anthony if they ever moved into their own house. When he was home, I found reasons to play outside just to get away from him.

One evening, just before supper, I wandered about a mile away from home, ending up on a little-traveled country road. The sun was setting, and I didn't know how to get back to my family. I looked about, hoping someone would be searching for me, calling my name. I supposed I was not missed, not even by Margie. As the evening cooled, I lay on the grass and pulled my legs up against my stomach to keep warm. I thought of Margie and how much I loved her, but now that she had Anthony, she no longer loved me, and I hated his menacing face more than ever. I began to sob.

As I lay shivering, I became aware of someone approaching. I must have dozed because the man on horseback was only a few feet from me when I heard the horse nicker. I sat up quickly, thinking it might be Papa searching for me. I stood, looking into the face of a stranger. He stopped his horse and peered down at me, smiling a sinister smile. Even though he scared me, I was happy to see someone who might take me home to my family.

I can't remember everything clearly after that, but over the years, bits and pieces have come to my mind, and I have been able to reconstruct the events of that evening and the next day. Some details are vague in my mind, but even as a five-year-old, the appearance of the man who stopped his horse to speak to me is as vivid now as the first time he uttered his first words.

"Well, what have we got here?"

I was too scared to speak.

"What are you doing out here by yourself, sweetie?"

I only remember saying, "I'm lost. I want Margie."

"Where do you live?" He asked, dismounting.

"I don't know." I pointed in the direction from which I thought I had walked."

He laughed. "Ain't no body lives in them woods. "How'd you get here?"

As I try to remember the events that followed, they all seem blurred. I recall the man walking toward me and scooping me up with one arm. He must have been very tall because he effortlessly remounted while holding me under his arm.

"Papa," I cried. "I want my Papa."

"I'm your papa now," the man chortled. He gave a sharp whistle, and the horse took off in a gallop.

I tried to speak, but my voice broke each time the horse's hoofs hit the ground. "Margie, Margie."

I cried quietly as the horse slowed to a gentle gait. I had no concept of praying on my own but tried to remember bits and pieces of prayers I had heard Papa pray when he was recovering from his poisoning. Over and over, I said Margie's name under my breath, asking her to come and find me.

After a few minutes, the man sat me on the saddle in front of him with one arm about my chest. We rode on and on for what seemed like an eternity. Darkness fell around us. I was cold and scared but happy to see streetlights when we approached the edge of a town, which I later learned was Scranton, Pennsylvania. I thought I would never see my family again.

We rode on for a few more minutes until we came to a small house surrounded by trees. There was a shed nearby. The man dismounted and lifted me off the saddle. He tied the reins to a railing and then took my hand, leading me to a wood door, which suddenly opened from the inside. A fat woman appeared in the doorway. Her face was not visible because the room was lit only by a single light bulb that dangled from the ceiling behind her.

Before the man could speak, she asked, almost shouting, "What you got here?"

The man didn't respond but took me by the hand and led me into the room. After we were inside, he pointed at a small child's rocking chair and told me to sit.

I obeyed, sitting quietly while the woman looked me over.

"Where'd you get her, Charlie?"

"Sittin' by the roadside, cryin' fer God sake. I guess she don't belong to nobody."

To this day, I don't know whether the woman, whose name I learned was Mildred, was angry or just concerned. "What we goin' to do with her? We can't hardly feed ourselves, Charlie."

"I don't know," the man said. "Fer God sake, I just couldn't leave her there, now, could I?"

"I just got a feelin' we're askin' fer trouble," the woman said, wringing her apron. "Didn't we have enough problems with Piney?"

Over the years, I have pondered about Piney and wondered who she might have been. The child's chair meant nothing to me then, but since I have been old enough to consider my plight at that time, I believe she might have been another child the couple kidnapped, or perhaps it was their own daughter who passed away or disappeared. I will never know, but I will always be grateful to Piney because she gave Charlie and Mildred reasons to be cautious with me.

Charlie appeared to mull over her question for a while, then said, "I'll figure out somethin'."

"Ya better start figgurin' fer God sake," she said. She walked to the side of the room and pulled a string to another lightbulb. In the new light, I could see the woman had a large scar down the side of her face. She spoke to the man. "You're hungry, I bet. And the little imp too."

"I would 'spect so," he said as he took a seat at a small kitchen table. "You know, Mildred, maybe I could sell her?"

She scoffed. "Who would buy that scrawny little child? She can't help nobody, just another mouth to feed, if you ask me, fer God sake."

I can't remember all that was said, but I understood enough to believe I would never see Margie or Papa again. I began to cry.

The woman set a plate of beans before me and commanded me to eat. I took two bites and then said. "I'm not hungry. Please, I want my Papa."

The man ate beans from a bowl, juice streaming from the corners of his mouth. He spoke with a mouth full of beans, chewed food falling onto his plate. "I told you I'm your papa, now didn't I?"

"But I don't want you for my papa."

"Fer God sake, Wilbur, you have to do somethin' about her. She spells trouble as sure as I been born. Somebody is goin' to hear her cryin'. Then what?"

He cursed as he got up from his seat. He walked over to a coat rack, slipped on a jacket, and donned a hat. "I told you I was goin' to sell her, didn't I? And I know someone who'll buy her, no questions asked."

He took me by the hand and led me toward the door.

"Good riddance, I say, fer God sake," the woman said as he closed the door after us.

The man held my hand as we strolled down the street.

"I'm cold." My voice quivered. "I want Margie."

We walked several blocks without speaking. I was so afraid, more afraid than when I saw the vision of Anthony at the foot of my bed. If I could get back home, I would tell him that I was sorry and that I would be glad to live with him and Margie.

On the corner, under a streetlight, was a policeman talking with a man, who walked away just as we approached. "Good evenin' officer," Charlie said. "Beautiful night, ain't it?"

"Yes, it is," the officer said, "And what a cute little girl you have there. Don't you think she needs a coat?"

"Yes, sir, but we live just down the street and will be home in a few minutes." He let go of my hand for a moment as he pointed in the direction we were walking.

I ran to the policeman and clung to his leg.

"What's wrong, honey?"

"I want my papa and Margie," I pleaded.

"She's just tired," the man said.

He grabbed me up in his arms and walked quickly down the street. Around a corner and out of sight of the policeman, he began to run. On the next corner was an empty house. The man turned toward the door and pushed it open. In the near-dark, he carried me upstairs to the end of a hallway, where he sat me on the floor. A window above my head allowed a nearby streetlight to cast light and shadows on the walls.

I heard his steps going down the stairs and knew I was alone. I was cold and hungry but afraid to leave the upstairs of the house. It seemed like an eternity before I fell asleep on the wood floor.

Chapter Seven

MYSTERIOUS WAYS

L ater, I was told that everyone was gathered around on our porch while Papa played "Nearer My God to Thee" and other songs of praise on his accordion. When the family sat down later to eat supper, Margie realized I was missing. After determining that I was not in the house, everyone searched outside. I understand that Jerome and Ralph ran to the barn to look for me. Anthony and Margie went to the well and shined a lantern to see if I had crawled on top of the box surrounding the well and fallen in. It was getting very dark by then, but Papa would not give up. He instructed Jerome to saddle our horse and ride up and down the road in front of our home, calling my name. I assume, by then, I had already been kidnapped and was on my way to Scranton. After two hours of searching, Papa gathered the family around the table and said a prayer for my safety.

"We will start again first thing tomorrow morning. I need to go to Scranton to check on an apartment Mrs. Walker told me about. Maybe Mr. Sherman will let me borrow a horse from him while the boys look for Anna. It is in God's hands now."

I slept on the wood floor all night long, waking because I was cold, and falling asleep again until daylight streamed through the window above me. I was so hungry but afraid to leave the building where Charlie had left me. I walked into a room facing the street and stood on my toes to peer out the window. There was a large house across from me with people streaming in and out.

I heard other people talking from somewhere in the building and was so afraid it might be Charlie. Later I learned I was in an apartment building, and a family lived next door. Cautiously, I walked down the stairs, holding onto the railing. At the front door, I peered out. With the door partly open, the aroma of food filled my nostrils. I was still wondering if my abductor was watching me, so I ran quickly across the street and squatted by the door. After a few moments, I stood, pushed open the door, and saw two long tables with men seated about them, having breakfast. I stepped inside and stood, watching the men eat. Finally, I walked over to the man closest to me and tugged on his sleeve.

"I'm hungry, Mister. Can I have something to eat?"

The bearded man appeared startled and amused. "Yes, honey, you sure can. Just a minute."

He turned his face toward a door across the room, cupped his hands about his mouth, and called a lady's name. "Emily."

A woman about my mother's age appeared in the doorway. "You want seconds, Henry?"

"Yes," he said, then pointed at me, "and bring this little tyke something. She looks like she's starved to death."

The woman, named Emily, came to the long table and knelt beside me. "What's your name, sweetheart?"

"Anna," I said, "and my Papa is named Daniel."

"Where is your papa?

"Home."

"Where is that? In Scranton?"

"No, not Scranton."

"Where then?"

"I don't know."

"Where is your mama?"

"I don't know," I said. "She left us."

The lady, Emily, took my hand. "You poor little thing. We will get you something to eat. Then we'll talk some more."

She sat me at a small table by the kitchen door and brought me ham, eggs, and biscuits. Nothing I had ever eaten tasted so good. After I finished, Emily came from the kitchen accompanied by another woman. As the other woman bent over me, I looked up into my mother's face, who, as it turned out, was running the boarding house.

I spent the next two nights sleeping with Mother. When I told her of my ordeal with Charlie and his wife, she thought I made it all up, but she had no explanation for me showing up in Scranton, where she was living and working. She ultimately decided a six-year-old child could not imagine such events. The next day, she made a report to the police, who promised to look for Charlie and his wife, but I believe they also had doubts about my story.

Mother was better to me than she had ever been at home,

but I missed Margie and the rest of my family and wanted to be with them. Mother promised me that she would get word to my father to come and get me, but God had His own plan for me.

On my third day at the boardinghouse, I looked out of the window and saw a horse and wagon down on the street. I couldn't believe my eyes when I saw Jerome and Loretta below my window. They were moving their belongings from the wagon into the apartment across the street, where I had been taken by Charlie. Thanks be to our God of miracles—we would all be united again. In all of Scranton, which was growing into a large city at that time with motorcars and electricity, somehow, my family found me. Papa had rented the apartment two days after I was abducted. God works in mysterious ways, leading me to my mother and my family. No one should doubt the power of His will. I have never doubted that it was God's hand that guided my father to the same apartment where Charlie had taken me. My father believed so and gave thanks to Jesus when he saw me. Only God knows how or why because He is in charge of all our lives.

When Papa learned that Mother was running the boardinghouse across the street from our apartment and sleeping with other men, he packed our wagon and moved our family back to Union Dale. He said he would look elsewhere for an apartment close to his work. I know Papa's heart was breaking, but he never let any of us know his true feelings about our mother.

WITH THE KIND OF LIFE WE LIVED, WE CHILDREN grew up fast. We had no other choice. Margie was married to Anthony, but I knew she didn't want to be. Although he seemed very thoughtful at times, he was usually gruff and cruel. I knew they would soon move into their own home, and I feared for her.

Papa's recovery from his arsenic poisoning was progressing slowly. It limited the time he was able to stand and work. Since our move back to Union Dale, he played his accordion at fewer venues. We all, even I, approaching the age of seven, had to pitch in. Since I was frail from rickets, I couldn't do much except care for Althea, who had begun to walk, although with difficulty. Still, I had an impossible task keeping her out of mischief.

When Althea tried to walk, she could not take a complete step with her left foot because she was very unsteady. She was cross-eyed and appeared to be mentally slow, but Papa loved her and thought her mischievous antics were cute. She often bit and scratched me, and when I retaliated, I was punished and sometimes sent to bed without supper. After Papa was asleep, Margie would bring food to me.

I think Papa blamed himself for Althea's condition, just as he had with Horton. He doted on her, constantly telling her she was sweet and adorable. He wouldn't allow anyone to correct her, regardless of her behavior. But for me, she was a little devil incarnate. I sometimes wished I was partially crippled and cross-eyed so Papa would be nicer to me.

"You be sweet to your little sister. Don't pick on her," Papa would say. "You know she isn't right."

I wasn't old enough to fully understand, but I believed she

was demon-possessed and knew exactly what she could get away with. I became her victim. My arms were seldom without fingernail marks and teeth bites. I prayed for the day I could get even. Sometimes when we were alone, I would let her have it. When I did, she would tell everyone I beat up on her, and I would be punished. Once, when we were sitting near Papa, she screamed that I had hit her. Without looking at me, Papa slapped me across the face, knocking me from my chair. My head hit the wall and knocked me unconscious for several seconds. When I came to, Margie was holding me and admonishing Papa for his cruelty toward me. She vowed then to take me with her when she moved out with Anthony.

On another occasion, just before supper time, I was sitting with Althea under the kitchen table. She jumped up and down and began screaming, "Anna is hurting me; she's kicking me."

She looked up and saw Jerome standing over us. Althea sat down beside me and held my hand. I felt as if I had been vindicated and that Papa would not punish me the next time my little sister made up stories about me. But it was not to be. The next day, Althea was biting and scratching me again, and Papa was cautioning me about my mistreatment of my sister.

Eventually Althea was diagnosed with a mental condition and was institutionalized in a state hospital in Scranton for a short while. My family came to believe she was a savant and not mentally ill at all. She was an avid reader and had an uncanny memory. At age forty, her eyes straightened, but she always had difficulty controlling her left leg when she walked. She was then sent to a state group home, where she spent the remainder of her life, dying at eighty. Years before she passed away, she professed Christianity, mainly due to our mother's influence.

She sent Althea Christian books for every birthday and Christmas. Even though our mother's life did not exemplify that of a true believer, she was instrumental in saving one of God's blessed children from a life of sin and eternal damnation. God does, indeed, work in mysterious ways.

Chapter Eight

MARGIE

Right after my seventh birthday, Margie and Anthony moved into a ground-floor apartment a few miles from Mr. Sherman's farm. Margie packed my meager belongings and took me with her when she and Anthony moved into their new apartment. It was sparsely furnished, with no running water and an outside toilet. We carried water from a community well and bathed in a galvanized tub Anthony brought from his mother's house. In winter, the house was always cold. I slept on a cot in the kitchen, which also served as our living room.

Margie was three months pregnant and often suffered from morning sickness and terrible back pains. Nevertheless, she was up early in the mornings, fixing Anthony's breakfast and packing him lunch for work. Later, she made breakfast for me and did her house chores without fail. I helped in every way possible, but I was frail and unable to make things much easier for my dear sister.

As I have said, Margie was more like a mother than a sister.

Long before I could speak, she rocked me and sang songs of praise. Because of her devotion, I was ever conscious of God's hand in my life, even when I was a baby. He revealed Himself to me through the songs my sister sang as she rocked me, a sickly child. I was suffering from what was later diagnosed as rickets. When we were alone in Margie's house, she sang all those songs over and over, and I learned all the verses as she sang. These verses would sustain me after Margie was called to be with Jesus.

It wasn't long before the terrible vision of Anthony I had seen at the foot of my bed revealed itself in our new home. After a few weeks, I learned I was in the way, and Anthony wanted me out of his house. Margie insisted that I must be with her because of my frail condition.

I could not start school when I turned six, but I was eager to learn. Because of the long distance to school, Margie taught me at home with the hope that I would be strong enough to walk to the actual school when I turned eight. Anthony was insistent that I be in school, which lasted a half day each day. So, Margie enrolled me. Some days she walked with me to school and waited in the back of the room until it was time for me to go home. When Anthony learned of this, he beat Margie and ordered her to send me home to my father. Margie refused. That night I heard her crying as Anthony beat her again. The following day, I told Margie I wanted to go live with Papa, but she knew my reason and vowed not to allow me to go, even if it meant her life.

I dreaded to see the evening come, knowing that Anthony would be home. Margie was such a good person and did her best to keep a clean house and prepare meals that would be waiting when he arrived home. Regardless of how much she tried, Anthony would fault her and slap her without warning. When she was six months pregnant, he threw her onto the floor because he did not like how she prepared his eggs for breakfast.

"You're a stupid woman, Margie. I don't know why I married you." He pointed at me. "And you put that damn little pest ahead of me in everything you do."

"No, I don't," Margie protested, "but I can't stand to see her mistreated at home. She has no one else but me."

"And me," he said. "Don't forget about me, your husband. I pay the damn bills and put a roof over your heads."

"I pray God forgives you, Anthony, for being so selfish and cruel."

"I'm not worried about God. I leave that to you."

Anthony built a three-cornered seat fastened in the corner of the kitchen to keep me out of the way. Over the bench, he hung an ominous razor strap. When he thought I deserved to be punished, he would force me to sit on the seat and dare me to move. He hit me across the back with the strap if I got up from the seat without his permission.

One evening I heard Margie crying because Anthony was beating her. I dashed out of the apartment to get help. Anthony caught up with me, hauled me back to the kitchen, and flung me onto the seat. He took the razor strap from the wall and drew it back to hit me. Margie heard my screams and ran into the room. She grabbed the strap and would not let go. Anthony took hold of Margie's hair and dragged her into the bedroom. I put my hands over my ears to shut out my sister's screams, but I still heard them in my head after I lay down to sleep that night.

At that time, Jerome was approaching eighteen. When he learned about Anthony's cruel behavior, he came to our house and demanded that Anthony come outside and face him man-to-man. Anthony came to the door with a shotgun under his arm but refused to go down the steps.

"I got no fight with you, Jerome, but I'm not gonna let you come to my house and threaten me or tell me how to treat my wife." He moved the shotgun from one arm to the other as if to threaten my big brother.

"You may have to kill me, Anthony Miller, because I will be back if you mistreat Margie or Anna again. If I ever hear that you laid a hand on my sister, I swear by Almighty God, I will kill you."

"I'm not gonna worry 'bout your threats, Jerome. I always liked you, but I'm sure not gonna forget this."

"And neither am I, Anthony." Jerome mounted his horse and turned for home.

Anthony raised the shotgun at Jerome's back and fired into the air. Jerome put his horse into a gallop. Anthony stepped down onto the ground and fired again, but by then, Jerome was well out of range of Anthony's gun.

While he was at the bottom of the steps, Margie closed and barred the door. She ran to the back of the house and ensured the door was also secured there.

Anthony attempted to break down the front door, then ran to the back of the house and thrust his shoulder against the door. He screamed and called Margie's name, threatening to kill both of us if he ever got into the house. When he realized

Margie was determined to keep him outside, at least until he stopped his rants, he begged her to unbar the door, promising never to mistreat her again. When that ruse failed, he threatened to burn down the apartment building with everyone in it. He carried straw to the front steps and ignited it, but Margie did not give in. When the straw burned out harmlessly without igniting the wood building, Anthony resorted to crying. He sat on the top step, with his face held in his hands, crying so loud Margie was afraid the other tenants in the building would hear.

"Poor thing," Margie said. She opened the door. "Come on in, honey, and I will fix you something to eat."

Margie set a bowl of beans and potatoes before us. We sat down to eat then Margie thanked the Good Lord for all our blessings. Anthony uttered the word "Amen," and then began to eat voraciously. It was the most peaceful time I had experienced in the house in a very long time. But after I went to bed, I heard Margie crying in her bedroom. She promised never to disobey Anthony again.

"Love, honor, and obey, the Bible says. Don't you know that, Margie?"

"Yes, I know that," she said.

"I think you forgot the obey part, but I will help you remember."

She was still sobbing when I fell asleep.

Margie began labor pains a month earlier than she expected. The pain in her back was continuous and severe. She begged Anthony to take her to see Doctor Williamson or to ask him to come to our house.

"It's just labor pains," Anthony said. "Christ, you might

think you was the only woman ever to have a baby. My mama sure didn't act that way."

"Please, Anthony. I'm in trouble," she pleaded.

"I'll go get the midwife. I can't afford no doctor."

"Please don't use the Lord's name in vain, Anthony. You will go to hell if you do."

"Don't you worry 'bout my soul," Anthony yelled back as he went out the front door. "Way you're carrying on sounds like you may need to be worrying 'bout your own soul."

I heard him chuckling as he went down the steps. I've never hated anyone but him, and God forgive me; I hated him more than ever then.

Several hours later, Anthony returned with Ellie, the same midwife who delivered Horton.

The midwife went to examine Margie. After a few minutes, she came out of Margie's bedroom and said, "She's been in labor too long. She will need a Caesarean."

"I'm not made of money. You need to birth the baby, Ellie."

At that moment, Margie began to cry out in pain. "I think the baby is coming. Thank God, it's coming."

I waited outside the bedroom with my face close to the door but heard Margie's cries for the next hour or more. Then there was silence. The midwife came out of the room. She was holding onto her apron and crying.

"Did the baby come?" I asked.

"Yes," Ellie said, "it came."

"Can I see it,"

"No, honey, it's dead. It's a boy, but he's dead."

I flung myself to the floor and cried with all my heart. I

know Margie wanted her very own baby, and now she would never have it. The vision of Anthony standing at the foot of my bed made me close my eyes tight, hoping I would never see him again. When I opened them, he was sitting at the kitchen table with his hands cupping his face, staring across the room at nothing.

The midwife called my name. "Anna, your sister wants to talk to you."

Margie was so pale. She could not raise her head, but she whispered to me, "I am going to be with Jesus, Anna, but don't you worry. I will look down on you and always keep you close to me. Remember, when I am gone, Jesus will never forsake you. Pray to him every day, just as we have always done."

"No, please, Margie. I love you so." I held her hand and laid my head next to hers on the bed. I could feel her shallow breathing. She never cried out or complained of pain. Twenty minutes later, my angel sister, Margie, smiled and breathed her last breath.

At the funeral, I was allowed to speak for a brief moment. But what does a child of seven say? My heart was bursting with pain and love for Margie. I prayed a child's prayer and opened my mouth. At first, no words came, then Jesus spoke through me, "A merciful God has taken Margie home to be with Him and spare her from her terrible life here on earth." I don't know where the words came from; they were His, not mine.

Chapter Nine

LIFE WITHOUT MARGIE

Margie's death was a terrible blow to my father, who loved her so dearly. He was still recuperating from arsenic poisoning with setbacks and painful bouts where his toes turned in more than usual. These repercussions persisted for years, probably until the day he died. His hands were never as agile as they were before his near-death experience. This condition made his accordion playing, which he loved, challenging, but it did not stop him from performing at dances when he had the opportunity. If I inherited anything from my father, I think it was his perseverance. Margie had done her best to be a mother to all of us since she was nine years old, and Papa was so happy for her when she found Anthony so she could finally have a life of her own. But Anthony brutalized her, and Papa blamed himself for her death.

Jerome talked of killing Anthony, and he might have if Papa had not intervened by reminding him of the damnation he would see on judgment day if he did. But Jerome still vowed that he would cripple him if he ever had the opportunity. I am certain I felt the same as Jerome, but as a small, weak child approaching just eight years of age, there was little I could do except despise that awful person. I knew then that the vision at the foot of my bed, months before, foretold what was to come, not to me, but to Margie. Long after her death, I felt I was, somehow, partly responsible for the terrible beatings she endured during her pregnancy. It was only after I lay awake for many nights praying for forgiveness that I accepted the fact I had done everything I could to save her from Anthony's cruelty. Knowing that Margie would want me to believe so gave me assurance I was still in God's sweet grace.

Two of my father's sisters wanted to take Althea and me to live with them, but Papa insisted that he wanted to keep us all together. Jerome became our guardian angel. He quit school before finishing the twelfth grade. He got a job building a fish hatchery, making just a few dollars a day, but essential to our existence. In addition to his job during the day and cooking meals in the evening, Jerome, with some help from Ralph, gathered and cut firewood for heating the house and cooking, but he kept the family together as Dad wished.

Father's paralysis returned from time to time as he slowly healed. Jerome contacted several doctors over that long period, none of whom could improve Dad's condition. The medical bills took much of Jerome's small earnings.

Jerome was always an easygoing, loving person. Somehow, he had always escaped Papa's unprovoked and unexpected temper outbursts. He loved our father. When Papa was first poisoned, and we all believed he might die, Jerome pleaded, "Please don't leave us, Dad, not when we need you so much."

God answered my brother's prayers and let Papa live. In many ways, our father's partial return to good health was due to Jerome's dedication to him. Regrettably, there would come a time when he was forced to confront Papa to save all of us from his ill temperament. I always believed he would have been more content and less harsh to his children if our mother were a more devoted wife. Although I never heard him say so, I think her rejection of him haunted him until his death.

Our family was destitute with mounting doctor bills and all needing clothes and food. The rent had to be paid. Ralph, who was fifteen, helped by doing odd jobs for neighbors, but Jerome bore the brunt of our problems. However, God takes care of His children, and He did so for us. A nearby Methodist deacon heard of our plight and set up credit for us at a local store where we bought groceries. When we moved from Union Dale, we owed the store more than one hundred dollars—a monumental amount in 1929 at the start of the Great Depression. The deacon's name was Mr. Hines, and I believe he never expected to be repaid for his kindness, but years later, Jerome repaid every penny with interest.

When our lives became desperate, we moved into a tiny three-room clapboard shack in Orson, Pennsylvania. There was a small kitchen and a room that functioned as a bedroom and living room; that is where Dad slept. All five of us children slept in the other room upstairs. There came a time when Papa was overcome by despair. He spent much of the money he made playing the accordion to buy sugar and potatoes for making homebrew, which he often drank until he was incoherent or intolerable. Many nights, we children were unable to sleep because of the noise coming from Papa's room while he and his drunken friends played checkers or told ghost stories until early in the morning. The stovepipe that came from the living room passed through our bedroom, carrying the voices with their vulgarity, making it seem as if the men were in the same room where we slept.

One such evening is etched in my memory. I was not only a sickly child but filled with fear. The ghost stories always brought back the vision of Anthony standing at the foot of my bed. I was afraid to go to sleep, so I lay awake at night staring up at the open attic hole in the ceiling. Rats infested the house, and when they moved about, I was sure Anthony would burst into the room and kill me. To make matters worse, my mother had warned us that some night when my father got really drunk, he would probably come into our room and put an end to all of us.

Loretta and Jerome found humor in the ghost stories we heard. They would make sounds and insist that the sounds were emanating from the dark shadows lurking in the room as we sat about the kitchen table before bedtime. The light glowing through the smoky glass chimney dimmed everything in the room. I was too scared to move from my chair by bedtime, but Jerome would force me to go to bed. I would stay awake until late at night, afraid Anthony was going to kill me if I went to sleep.

In fits of rage, Mother had often told me, "God will punish you." And when Althea and I were fighting, Loretta used the same expression. "God doesn't want sisters to fight; he will punish you if you do."

"It isn't my fault," I would say, "Althea is devil possessed. She won't stop biting and scratching me."

One time my father intervened. He kicked me and knocked me unconscious. I woke up cradled in Jerome's arms.

"No more, Dad. You aren't going to mistreat her anymore."

It did my heart good to have Jerome protect me, but it hurt so much when Papa cried and said the devil had gotten into his soul and he would never hurt one of his children again. His demeanor changed for a while, but before long, he was as unpredictable as ever. His recovery from paralysis was slow. At first, he crept about slowly, then, later, he walked on crutches. I believed God was punishing him for his drinking and terrible temper. He was still unable to control his anger at times and once struck Loretta with his fist because he believed she was emptying his cider barrel. She was only screwing on the cap but paid for that with an abrasion over her eye.

I have always believed that Papa partially lost his mind after suffering arsenic poisoning and then losing Margie. Despite his erratic temper and unprovoked outbursts, we children loved our father and knew he loved us much more than our mother did.

Interlude

The clock down the hall chimed nine times, reminding me I had been engrossed in Anna's memoir for nearly two hours. I stopped reading, sat back in my chair, and envisioned a frail little girl whose life in the early part of the twentieth century was one of meager survival, brutality, and fear. It was easy to imagine that same little girl with her nose pressed against the fish tank at the Westwood Convalescent Center in Ypsilanti, Michigan. Her question to me, asking if I thought there would be fish in Heaven, came to mind. I understood how she came to ponder that question.

In Anna's mind, I think, she believed that if God brought her through the travails of her early life, all things are possible with Him, and in His Heaven, all creatures will be welcome. It is difficult to comprehend how her father and mother, whose lives were in disarray, could pass on the concept of Jesus Christ and God to their children. Perhaps they feared hell and damnation but believed in redemption, even for the worst of sinners. Somehow, the same fear which they passed on to Anna was transformed into faith, love, and devotion in that little girl. And out of a thoroughly dysfunctional existence, Anna discovered a faith that sustained her in childhood and throughout her adult life.

I set down Anna's memoir, changed into my pajamas, and prepared for bed. I intended to begin reading again at that time, but the spectra of that frail little girl would not leave my mind. I put the book down again and wondered how I would now view Anna and what I would say to her the next time we met at the fish tank. I would have in me a recognition of her strengths and determination, respect for her intelligence, and admiration for her accomplishments despite the obstacles she had faced in life. I fell asleep, contented that such a good soul as Anna had come into my life.

The next morning, I performed my usual tasks for my wife, then walked down the hallway toward Anna's room. She was playing "Amazing Grace" on her harmonica, something she did almost every morning. I waited until she appeared, pushing her walker ahead of her. There was no indication that she was aware of my presence as she made her way to the patient lounge area and aquarium, her sanctuary. There was an aura about her. Even with the vagaries of dementia, she maintained a dignified and humble demeanor of a saint. The story, *The Song of Bernadette* by Franz Werfel, came to mind. Like Saint Bernadette, Anna's life was one of suffering and sacrifice. And through it all, Anna held no animosity for anyone. I slowly backed away, leaving her to her thoughts and prayers. That night, I would read again about the remarkable woman I had come to love and respect.

Chapter Ten

CATASTROPHE AND CURE

When I was nine, I attended a small school near Orson. There were only twelve students in my class. Most of them were from poor families, but none were as destitute as mine. I think our teacher also came from a poor family and understood our plight. Often, when the weather was favorable, she took us out into the fields to find winter greens, wild grapes, and other things we could eat. It made me realize that other children who went to my school might not have enough to eat, just like my family. All of us were happy to be outside and hopeful of finding something good to eat that we could take home to our families.

One winter day, when the sun was shining, we went into a field where a pond was frozen over with thick ice. While we were all playing on the ice, my feet slipped from under me. I fell backward, striking my head on rocks. I was a little dizzy but able to walk back to the school. I sat at my desk and soon realized that my sight was slowly fading. The condition continued for the remainder of the day. Just before school let out, I was almost blind. The sun was shining on the red hair of the girl sitting in front of me, but I couldn't see the teacher's face at the front of the class. I began to pray silently, *Please, Jesus, don't let me lose my sight. I won't be able to get home tonight.* I wanted to scream that I was going blind, but I was afraid to talk without the teacher's permission. I sat in fear for several minutes, then whispered to the red-haired girl, "I can't see."

The girl in front of me looked over her shoulder and saw me crying. "What's wrong, Anna?"

"I can't see. I think I'm going blind."

She jumped to her feet and cried, "Something is wrong with Anna."

By then, my stomach was convulsing. I tried to stand but was too dizzy. The teacher came to my desk and helped me onto the floor.

"Lie still," she said, "and see if you feel better."

I lay quietly, but my dizziness and urge to vomit continued. The teacher, whose name I have forgotten, dismissed the class. She spoke quietly, but I was so disoriented I had no idea what she was saying. Two of the neighbor boys walked me home. One held my hand and described what was in front of me with almost every step I took. That was the first time any boy was kind to me, and I have never forgotten him. His name was Roy, and since then, I have always thought Roy was a beautiful name for a boy.

I don't remember being put to bed or having anything to eat for several days. Although Papa couldn't afford to pay, he sent for a doctor. When I was well enough to talk, Jerome told me I suffered a concussion and was blind for three days.

According to the doctor, it was a miracle I survived my head injury. But God was my physician even though my family and I had almost given up on Him. From that experience, I learned that in moments of desperation, most people will call on the God they deny in their daily lives.

God has a way of reminding us that He is in charge. To this day, I often have a ringing in my ears. It is a little memento God gave me to remind me that by all reasoning, I should have died that day. But God was not through with me then, and He is not through with me now. Later, I was examined by an ear specialist who determined that the damage was permanent. Perhaps so, but even at my age of eighty-four, God will cure the long-lasting effects of the concussion if He chooses. That prerogative is His, and I willingly accept whatever He has planned for me.

When Althea turned six, she started school. Because of her inability to walk without assistance, I pulled her in a small wagon, and I remember that both of us had new dresses purchased from Sears and Roebuck for ninety-eight cents each. How proud and happy we were to be dressed like some of the other girls. The other students made fun of us even though our dresses were as nice as any other girl in our school. We wore the same size dresses even though I was almost eleven years old. I was a picture of malnutrition, skin, and bone, with a pallid complexion. It was only by the grace of God that I stayed alive and was able to pull my disabled sister to school.

Jerome took me to two different doctors because I was in such poor physical condition. One doctor had no idea why I was so undernourished when all my siblings seemed to be in relatively good health, considering the conditions under which we lived. One doctor told Jerome, "This child has rickets. She needs lots of vitamin C."

On one occasion, Jerome bought a dozen oranges, intended for me, but we all shared them because we seldom had such good things to eat. Maybe he bought them again. I just don't remember.

Another doctor believed I had been given sour milk as a baby and in my early childhood. For years, the thought of drinking milk revulsed me. One night, I dreamed that milk tasted so very good. When I awoke, I was thirsty, and could hardly wait to taste milk. I still remember how delicious it was. Afterwards, I drank it at every meal if we were fortunate enough to have some in our home. I began to put on weight and gain some height. Before long, I was looking more like a girl than a little scarecrow.

How did I come to love the taste of milk after years of refusing to drink it? You will hear me say over and over that things happen for a reason, and everything is possible with God. There is no doubt in my mind that God gave me that dream and helped me cure the rickets that had plagued me all my life.

My health was finally improving, and I had more energy than ever before. I could now eat a meal without crying, which I had often done. During those times, Papa grew very impatient with me.

"Eat your supper, Anna, and quit your whining."

"Nothing tastes good, Papa, but I'm still hungry.'

"Eat!" he said emphatically.

If I failed to eat as quickly as he wished, Papa would shout louder, place his hand on my forehead, and slam my head against the wall. It has occurred to me that the many times my father did this may have made me vulnerable to the concussion I suffered when I was nine. If so, I forgive him even now.

During that time, we had very little to eat, and that was usually one meal a day with some crackers or cornbread before we went to bed at night. Loretta prepared scrambled eggs in the morning and usually burned them. The home-fried potatoes seemed never to be done enough. But we were all still grateful for her efforts. She could never care for us the way Margie did, but she tried. Later her cooking skills improved. Either that, or we just got used to her cooking.

Chapter Eleven

HORSES

After Margie passed away, Jerome took me under his wing. Because of my fragile health, he often did tasks that were assigned to me as an eleven-year-old. When he did his evening chores, he always took me with him, explaining how to feed the horse, and being careful not to stand directly behind our old mare, Nellie, while she ate. I would take a position near Nellie's head. One evening when the horse was particularly cantankerous, I turned my back and she bared her teeth and bit me on my cheek, breaking the skin. After that, I stood far away while Jerome fed and watered the old horse. But my brother would not give up. He insisted that my experience with Nellie was a freak accident and would not happen again. Before long, I regained my courage and was feeding Nellie on my own.

I don't know where the money came from, but somehow, Papa and Jerome bought another horse. In the spring, Jerome and Ralph plowed fields for our neighbors, making a few dollars that we really needed. Because of my newfound courage in caring for Nellie, Jerome put me in charge of the team of horses. I grew very fond of my charges, and asked Jerome if I could learn to ride one of them. He agreed and put me on the new horse, Jasper, in front of him. Jasper took two steps forward and then reared into the air, dumping me and Jerome onto the ground with a thud. Luckily, I fell on top of Jerome, who insisted that he wasn't harmed in the slightest way.

I have come to realize that Jerome was doing everything he could to normalize my life. I know that he did not need my help and that it was a lot of trouble for him to include me and constantly look out for me. But I am so thankful to a gracious God for such a loving brother. Unfortunately, Jerome could not always be at my side to protect me from the vicissitudes of life or Papa's frequent cruelty.

Our school was three miles away, and it was my job to get Althea to her classes. As I previously mentioned, she had difficulty walking. I pulled her in a small wagon on roads that were barely passable. When it rained, the continuous horse, wagon and car ruts made my task nearly impossible. Only my prayers, and strength given to me by Jesus Christ, enabled me to pull the wagon with my crippled sister in it. In the winter, when it snowed, the road was impassable unless it was cold enough to freeze the ground. I wore cloth gloves, but my hands ached from the cold by the time we arrived at school.

One morning, after a deep snowfall, Papa decided it was too cold for Althea to go to class. By the time school was dismissed, we were experiencing a raging blizzard. I walked home with my head down, staying close to a fence that ran along a field near the road. A team of horses overtook me. I didn't hear them coming. They were driven by a young man who was shielding his face and eyes from the terrible snowstorm, and he could not see where his team was going. The horses veered to the side of the road and knocked me over. In the confusion, they reared into the air with their hooves coming down near me. I prayed to Jesus Christ to save me. There is no logical explanation of what happened next except that God intervened. The horses suddenly calmed down and stopped in their tracks. I rolled to one side and got to my knees. I realized then that God had plans for me. He had stopped the horses and enabled me to roll to safety. Since then, I have feared horses.

When I arrived home, I could not locate my arithmetic book. Papa was furious with me because he knew the school would demand that I pay for the book. He vowed that, no matter what, he would not waste our few dollars on the textbook I lost.

"Why are you so addlebrained, Anna?"

His remarks cut into my soul. "I'm sorry, Papa. The horses almost killed me."

I was certain the book was in the snow where the horses reared above me. Jerome and I rode Jasper to the spot and looked for it, but we were unable to find the book.

Each day in school, the teacher reminded me that I would have to pay for the book, but we had no money to spare. I had no textbook to work from and was unable to complete assignments at home. I prayed to God to help me find it. That spring, when the snow melted, with Jerome's help, I searched along the fence where I had fallen. By the grace of God, I found the book.

As we made our way back home on Jasper, a horse and

rider came our way. As he got closer, I recognized Anthony when he began speaking to Jerome.

"How you doing, Jerome?"

I know my brother did not wish to speak with the man who caused Margie's death, but Jerome, was such a good person, right up until he died of cancer at the age of sixty-five.

"Alright," he responded, "and how are you, Anthony?"

Anthony slowed his horse and shouted back over his shoulder. "Good," he said.

"Just want you to know, I'll be gettin' married next month." His voice trailed off as the horse moved on down the road.

I looked into Jerome's eyes. Tears ran down his face. "I wonder who he intends to marry, poor girl."

"I hate that awful man, I said. "Do you think Jesus minds if I do?"

"Probably not. Jesus probably hates him too."

"No, Jesus loves all of us, saints and sinners alike."

"That doesn't stop me from hating the bastard."

He kicked Jasper in the flank. The horse took off at a gallop.

Chapter Twelve

FAITH AND FAILURE

We had not heard from our mother for several weeks but understood she was still living in Scranton and perhaps running the boarding house. Our father stopped making homebrew, maybe because he could no longer afford to buy ingredients. Our credit account at the small grocery store was far more than our ability to pay at the time. I have always believed that this was why Papa stopped drinking as much as usual, and not that he had a change of heart or feared retribution for a sinful life.

At that time, we did not attend church or observe any religion, but my life was about to change with a reintroduction to Jesus Christ. One evening, an evangelist by the name of Domenic Castaldo knocked on the door of our ramshackle house. He was holding a revival at the Methodist Church in Orson and invited us to attend. Reverend Castaldo was very persuasive and convinced Jerome to put all of us in our two-seater wagon and take us into Orson for the revival.

The reverend was a graduate from Practical Bible College

in Johnson City, New York, and he had acquired speaking skills more persuasive than most country preachers I heard as a child. I remembered his mannerisms much more than the texts of his sermons. When he shouted, my heart would almost leap out of my chest. The wonder of the preacher's voice sent me into another world. It was there, at the age of twelve, that I realized all the slights and difficulties of my childhood happened for good reasons and were leading me to the arms of Jesus Christ. I accepted Him one night during the revival, and I have leaned on Him ever since. Although my life has not been without problems and disappointments, Jesus has never let me down.

The church impressed me with the huge lights and stained-glass windows. After each service, I dreaded returning to our dilapidated shack, and would have been happy never to leave the sanctuary of that little church. As I look back on that time, I realize my heart was filled with envy, and that I should have been grateful to God for the roof my family had over our heads. And even though our experience with Reverend Castaldo eventually proved disappointing, I will always appreciate his invitation that led me back to Jesus.

At the beginning of each service, a small choir with piano accompaniment played. I heard the music and words to "The Old Rugged Cross" and "Since Jesus Came into My Heart," which I especially loved. When I was overcome with joy, I sang along with the choir to the top of my frail voice. The week of the revival brought a sense of belonging I had never experienced.

After we attended services the first two nights, the preacher insisted that Jerome bring our father to the next service, but Papa refused to come. Reverend Castaldo sent a Bible home to

Papa, and Jerome encouraged him to read it. It became my daily task to turn the pages while he read. Papa liked to smoke his pipe, so I learned how to fill it for him. Those were times when I felt close to Papa and silently forgave him for his frequent temper eruptions and cruelties to me and my siblings. But there came a time when Satan stepped in and set back all the good works and wonders of the revival.

A few days before the revival ended, we all went to the altar and professed our faith in Jesus as our Savior. Ralph and I eagerly accepted the tenants of the Methodist Church and agreed to be baptized the following Sunday morning. But Loretta and Jerome were reluctant. Reverend Castaldo told me I would have to say something about confessing my sins and accepting Jesus when I was baptized. That troubled me, and I spoke to my father about it. He understood and said, "Just say, Jesus said, 'Suffer not the little children and let them come unto me, for such is the kingdom of Heaven.'"

At my baptismal, I remembered those words and added my own. "I am only a child, but I want to come to Jesus."

Reverend Castaldo spoke with Jerome and Loretta and finally convinced them to be baptized. When we arrived home that evening after the service and began discussing our renewed faith, we learned the reverend had been untruthful in his efforts to recruit Loretta and Jerome to the church. He told Loretta that Jerome had agreed to be baptized if she also would. When she agreed, he had a discussion with Jerome, using the same tactics to convince him to be baptized. After concluding that Reverend Castaldo was a fraud, we never attended the Methodist Church in Orson again. But I held onto the belief that Jesus had come into my life despite my disappointment in the reverend. I was happy I had attended his revival. It showed me, once again, God works in mysterious ways.

My dad's health continued to improve slowly, and he was able to play his accordion more frequently. This was about the time he resumed making homebrew and staying up until early morning hours, playing checkers with our neighbors. I never understood why our little shack was the gathering place for these men. Perhaps it was because their wives would not allow drinking in their homes. I believe Papa might have been happy to live with the same constraints if our mother had stayed home with him. I never heard him accuse Mother or blame her for his paralysis; none of us children dared to broach that possibility in his presence.

Sometimes, in the early morning hours after checkers, I could hear Father saying his prayers. He always asked God to bless our mother and "direct her feet toward home and her children." After his "Amen," I added my own and promised God I would always love my unhappy father. I wondered if Mother ever prayed for Papa. I suppose not.

Two weeks after the revival ended, we learned that Anthony had married a sixteen-year-old girl from Orson by the name of Brenda Morgan. Her father had died the year before in a logging accident, leaving her mother to care for Brenda and six brothers, all younger than she. The subject of Anthony was mentioned briefly at our supper table that evening, but quickly ended when Papa said he did not want to hear anything about Anthony.

"That subject is too painful for me to think about."

Jerome spoke up. "I would like to kill the bastard."

Papa shushed Jerome and reminded him again that hell and

damnation awaited anyone contemplating or committing murder. "You don't want to burn in hell, son."

"He killed my sister, and I will never forgive him. I hope something terrible comes his way."

Tears welled in Papa's eyes. "That won't bring back our Margie."

I said, "She's an angel now, isn't she, Papa?"

"She always was." He got up from the table and went to his bedroom. I heard him sobbing. Then he broke into a coughing spell before quieting down.

"I may not kill him," Jerome said after Papa left the table, "but I sure hope someone does, and real soon."

Chapter Thirteen

BITTERNESS SETS IN

From time to time, my dad would suffer renewed pain because his toes turned under his feet, and his fingers developed crippling arthritis. When his pain became unbearable, he drank homebrew and moonshine, when he could buy it, to kill his pain. When he attempted to play his accordion, he wept silently. He blamed God for his problems and lashed out at all of us children. However, we all knew it wasn't God who crippled him; it was our mother.

While Jerome, Ralph, and Loretta struggled to keep our family together, Althea continued having difficulties walking and appeared to have problems with mental illness. I began to outgrow my frailties, but still suffered from a ringing in my ears from my concussion. I attempted to hold onto my beliefs in God and Jesus, but my father rebuffed my offers to turn the pages of the Bible while he read. I missed those small moments of closeness to my father and prayed to Jesus, asking Him to make Papa believe again.

For several months, not one of us dared bring up the

subject of God or the Bible. Papa was the only one in our family who dared to broach the subject of religion, and that was always in a negative way. He was determined that all of us should question God's existence or, at least, rebuff the idea that He was good.

"What has God ever done for me or any of you children? If He exists, He has caused me nothing but pain and misery."

I went to the table by Papa's chair and picked up the Bible, saying, "Jesus loves you, Papa, and He will make things better if you believe."

Papa reached for the Bible, took it from my hand, and threw it across the room. But there would come a time in his later life when he asked me to read Psalms to him. I have always believed that a planted seed will eventually sprout to fruition no matter how formidable the weather it has faced. Although the small seed planted by Reverend Castaldo lay dormant for many years, it began to bear fruit in my father's elderly years. But when I was twelve, Papa was more like a disciple of Satan than that of Jesus. And although Jerome and I were reluctant to follow our father down his sinful path, Ralph and Loretta took up Papa's mantle and blasphemed Jesus and the idea of God. My heart was pained, but I continued to pray for my father and dear brothers and sisters.

Though I faced continued opposition, I wanted to be sure that I would go to Heaven someday. I remembered the songs Margie taught me and those I learned at the revival meetings, but Papa wanted me to keep silent. He threatened to punish me if he ever heard me singing "Since Jesus Came into My Heart." He said, "That garbage in the Bible about 'Be strong and of good courage' is for other people and not for us."

"God only cares for the haves, not the have-nots like us." He emphasized by thumping his hand on the table. When he did that, I almost jumped off my seat in fear.

He was my father, and the Bible commanded me to honor my father and my mother, but I could not. I began to believe I was sinning by not believing as he wanted. I understood Papa's point; we were constantly wondering where our next meal was coming from. Not only was I hungry for food, but I also hungered to know if there was a chance for me in Heaven.

I was glad that I learned to read early in life. One day while I was rummaging around in that house, I found a book. As I leafed through it, my eyes fell on a picture of an old-fashioned girl wearing a muddy dress. She was kneeling in prayer. The pages of the book were brown with age. I never learned its origin, but I believe an angel, perhaps my Margie, left it for me to find. There was a prayer that I learned and said to Jesus. It was the best I could do. At that moment, all my father's blasphemy fell away, and I was ushered into the presence of Jesus.

Now the morning's come, I'll raise
All my thanks to God in praise
Thank thee, Jesus, Lord Divine
For the sleep that has been mine
Guard and keep me every hour
By thine own almighty power
Help me to obedient be
Unto those placed over me
Young I am, and weak, and so
What is best I cannot know

Teach my heart to look to thee
Oh, how good I'll try to be

That poem changed my life. Thereafter, nothing, not even Papa's bitterness, could keep me from knowing and praising Jesus. I was determined to be as saintly as possible. I would show love to my brothers and sisters and compassion and forgiveness to my father, no matter his cruelty or impatience with me. I would make a difference in my family's life. I would prove to Papa that all things are possible with God. I would be courageous and of good cheer.

When I went downstairs, Loretta was busy in the kitchen.

"Can I help you, sister?"

Loretta seemed dismayed. "What has come over you, Anna?"

I explained how I found the poem and how it transformed my life. I told her I wanted to be of good cheer and to show my love for her and my other brothers and sister. I had committed the poem to memory and quoted it for her.

I explained as only a child can. "God talked to me. He will help Papa and all of us if we have faith."

Loretta came to me and placed her arms about me. "I love you, sister. What you have done is so nice. You must keep on saying the poem." She was fourteen. I imagine she never expected anything as profound as that poem could be appreciated by a twelve-year-old. I wanted to recite the poem for my father, but I knew he would not allow me to get past the first verse before telling me it was garbage.

I said the poem every day, often several times each day. I know God heard me. On a wall behind the table hung the Ten

Commandments, surrounded by flowers, angels, and ovals, along with the Lord's Prayer. I stared at this beautiful representation of God's love. Jerome earned the poster by selling Cloverine salve before we attended Reverend Castaldo's revival. It is a miracle that the poster survived Papa's rejection of God and the Bible. I believe it indicated that Papa still held a kernel of belief despite his claim of agnosticism.

After my renewed dedication to Jesus, the poster helped shape my life. Every child should have this privilege of reading the Ten Commandments and Lord's Prayer every day, as did I. I vowed always to remember God's laws even if no one else would obey Him. There were, and still are, many temptations, and God delivered me from all of them. I praised Him as a child and still praise Him today.

I believed if I remained steadfast, God would see me through every pitfall of life and that He would open the eyes of my father and even direct Mother's feet toward home and her children as my Papa had often prayed before his bitterness set in. That did not happen, but I never stopped praying for it. God's will is God's will, and I accept it.

Chapter Fourteen

MOTHER COMES HOME

During thirty-five years of marriage and the loss of five children, my mother and father moved forty times. Each time, we believed we were making a fresh start where no one would know about our mother's discredited reputation. She committed some awful sins, the worst of which was the frequent abandonment of her husband and children. Yet, as I think of the relationship between my parents, I have some empathy for my mother, and I can see why she might have found it difficult to be loyal to my father. It was a different matter with her children, who loved her despite her frequent and prolonged absences from our lives.

When my parents were young, my father was in love with Aunt Cora, my mother's younger sister, and wanted to marry her. Her father was determined that she, his eldest daughter, age nineteen, should marry first. Papa wanted a wife. Since our mother was a beautiful young woman, he married her. I think neither of them knew much about the other at the time. It must have taken a while for them to get really acquainted. Even though Papa learned to love my mother, I have never believed she returned his love.

Continual poverty can have a devastating effect on any relationship. My father was accustomed to it from the time he was a young boy. He was orphaned at the age of ten and had a very difficult life, being passed from relative to relative and eventually living with an older couple who worked him like an adult. He ran away at fifteen and found work in a saloon.

Jobs were difficult to find, and father accepted almost any type of work available while he and Mother clothed and fed five children. He was an excellent musician and played the piano, guitar, and accordion. When he was offered an opportunity to play for dances in Scranton every night, he eagerly accepted, telling Mother he would be home each week for at least one night. But she was left alone in Hawley, Pennsylvania to raise their five children. Dad sent money home, but she saw him only once or twice during the next six months. Undoubtedly, that was the beginning of their marital problems.

When I was twelve, we moved to a backwoods farm in White Mills, Pennsylvania. I will never forget the joy I felt when I saw the large house we were moving into. To us, it was a mansion compared with the rickety small dwelling we left behind. A kind gentleman heard of our situation and came to our shack to offer the farmhouse to Father. In addition to the large house, the gentleman informed us that work might be available to Jerome and Ralph in one of the mills there.

Althea and I rode in his truck as he moved our furniture and belongings. We were all so excited about our new home.

We talked optimistically about the opportunity to make our lives better. It was truly a blessed day, and I thanked God for it.

That winter, we learned the clapboard shack we left behind burned to the ground. We were all happy that we moved out and did not go down with the shack. The new house had four bedrooms, but we had very little furniture to put in them. Still, we were so happy to have privacy and space to breathe. There was a covered porch, which kept deep snow from piling up around our front door. At our small house in Orson, when it snowed, Jerome would have to jump out of the upstairs window to shovel snow away from our door to allow all of us to go outside.

Our farmhouse sat on several acres, and we had no neighbors other than a German lady with her two sons, whose house was between us and the town of White Mills. We wanted to be friends with her and her family, but she declined our invitation to join us for a bonfire celebration. We were fortunate that our invitation was not accepted. We learned that her sons had been arrested for burglary many times and that they were frequently in barroom brawls. So we left them alone, and our family remained isolated from most of society until we children were old enough to leave home on our own.

A few days after moving in, Althea and I enrolled in school. It seemed much larger than our school in Orson. With its four spacious rooms, it made me think of it as a major city school, which I had heard about. The road from our house was full of ruts and was muddy, much like our roads in Orson. I still had the responsibility of pulling Althea to school in a wagon. She could walk a little with difficulty, and it was my job to hold onto her as we took each step.

Both Althea and I had problems adjusting to our new school because the grades were much more advanced than in our old school. The teacher took no pity on either of us and frequently berated Althea and me for not understanding some elements of our lessons. She seemed intent on making me look dumb before the class. I often prayed to Jesus about the teacher's apparent intentional efforts to embarrass me.

I remembered He had said to me, "have faith and be of good cheer." By the end of the school year, my teacher told me how proud she was of my progress and that I was the most determined student in her two classes.

"Your grades are not the best, but you try harder than anyone else I teach. I am so proud of you for that."

She included a short note to my father with my report card, telling him of my progress. I thanked her and promised to try even harder. I didn't believe I could do better, but that was the only thing I could think to tell her.

Our mother came to live with us and stayed for a few months. She shunned my father and slept in bed with Loretta. Even so, Papa's health improved, and he started playing the German accordion for dances. He encouraged Jerome to accompany him on the fiddle. Our brother Ralph played the piano, guitar, and accordion, so the Duvalls formed a band, which became popular in White Mills. Everything went well for a while until Papa took up drinking again. Ralph became disgusted with our father and formed his own band. Our mother left home again, and misery overtook our family as Dad became more erratic and unpredictable.

We children attended all the dances Ralph and Jerome played for because we were afraid to stay at home alone with our father. It was good to see Jerome and Ralph in their element, playing music and forgetting the problems we all knew awaited us when we arrived back home. I began to square-dance at the age of twelve and became quite good at it. We had no other enjoyable diversions except an occasional Sunday afternoon baseball game.

School continued to be hectic. By the time we arrived each morning, I was exhausted from pulling Althea. People were often cruel, especially when they learned of my mother's abandonment of her family and our alcoholic father.

Dad often drove his horse and buggy into town. He parked in the churchyard shed and spent the afternoon in a saloon. Sometimes he carried his accordion and played music for the bar patrons. He earned no money for playing, but his friends kept him in beer.

After school, Althea and I waited outside the saloon for hours so we could ride home with our father. We were so embarrassed at times because he was abusive to us and lashed out at people on the street, calling them *dummies* and *ignorant* because they happened to be passing by while he staggered toward the churchyard to get his horse and buggy. In the winter, Althea and I would be frozen stiff by the time we climbed onto the wagon, hugging each other to keep warm, while Papa cursed at Jasper to "get a leg on."

Adding to our embarrassment and harassment at school was news of our mother's arrest. At Christmas, she came home with gifts for the boys and dolls for the girls. We thought we would have the best Christmas in years, but the police came to our house and took the gifts away. They arrested Mother. She was charged with stealing everything from a department store in Scranton. She was confined to the city jail for eight months. Only Jerome visited her, and just once, during her incarceration.

Her arrest made newspaper headlines. The charges gave our classmates more ammunition to taunt us. They were such cruel children. If only one of them could have endured what Althea and I were subjected to at home, our classmates might have been kinder. The prospect that we would experience such cruelty put dread into my soul every morning as I struggled with the wagon, pulling Althea behind me. When I attempted to sleep at night, I still heard their jeering and mocking in my head. By reciting the Twenty-Third Psalm, I was able to find peace for a few hours, but would wake up with the taunts of my classmates filling my head. I wanted to love everyone and asked God to forgive me for my sins because I hated my schoolmates with every fiber of my being. They mistreated Althea because of her physical ailments, sometimes spitting on her and tripping her when she attempted to walk.

We were often persecuted by cruel boys who walked along the road we traveled to and from school. One morning, Althea and I talked and decided we could not endure such cruelty any longer. We told Papa what we were experiencing. Our father wrote a letter to the principal, who put a stop to our mistreatment for a while.

We still attended school every day after that but were shunned by our classmates. I supposed they thought we would report them if they taunted us again, and we might have done so. School was never pleasurable for us, but it was no longer unbearable. I learned from that awful experience that children often pay for the sins of their parents. I vowed that if I ever had children of my own, I would never do anything to cause them embarrassment or pain. I hope I have accomplished that so far in my life.

Chapter Fifteen

QUITTING SCHOOL – FINDING GOD

When spring came, Papa cleared four acres of land. He pulled up stumps and cleaned and burned brush dotting the field. I helped plant seeds and cultivate the soil. He left alcohol alone. He was kind to me and complimentary of my hard work. We got acquainted during those long days. He told me about his past as an orphan and how he met my mother and learned to love her. I came to realize that inside him was a caring man with deep regrets for the way his life unfolded. It gave me a new perspective on my father and mother. I came away from that experience knowing that he saw in me traits of honesty and decency that would sustain me throughout my life.

That spring, working in the field with my father made me think about getting a job to make money for myself and my family. I didn't return to school after graduating from eighth grade. However, I was concerned about the abuse Althea might receive without me there to protect her. I talked with her teacher, who understood some of the taunting we had endured the previous year. She agreed to look after Althea and not reveal her actual last name to the other students because of our mother's sullied reputation.

For a while, I worked for a family, looking after their children, housecleaning, and assisting the mother, who was frail. The father was a bully and very abusive, worse than anything I had been subjected to with my own dad. He kept his poor wife in tears, and his two young daughters cowered from him when he was yelling and screaming. I wanted to help the mother and children, but I didn't dare meddle in their family affairs. When I could no longer endure witnessing such abuse, I quit working for them. The wife begged me to stay, telling me her husband behaved better when I was with her. But Jerome was concerned about my safety and wanted me to quit that job. I had little choice and could do nothing except ask God to protect them after I was gone.

Our country was in the middle of a great depression, and jobs were hard to find. Luckily, I heard that a local silk mill in White Mills was hiring, and I applied. The girl who interviewed me was dressed very fashionably and carried herself with a superior air. I will never forget the name of Beatrice Tyree and how uncomfortable she made me feel.

"You poor little country waif. You won't ever make it here. I give you no more than six months before you throw up your hands and quit, and you will never be the same."

Beatrice Tyree was right—I would never be the same. Her words didn't deter me but made me more determined than ever to succeed. As soon as I learned the rudiments of the job, I was performing as well as the employees with much more experience. I hoped Beatrice was noticing my progress.

The depression worsened, and competition for jobs was threatening all of us. I agreed to a reduction in pay to seven dollars each week. My work hours were from seven a.m. until five p.m. each weekday. Whatever I made was divided three ways, one-third going to my father and one-third to Loretta for groceries. I kept one-third for myself.

After work, I walked three miles through the woods to our home. When it rained, I was usually soaked to the skin when I reached our front porch. One evening, I was accosted by the bully who made my life miserable at school. I learned he often walked along part of the same path. He followed me for the last mile, taunting me with names he had called me at school. He caught up and tugged at the hem of my coat. I stopped and faced him.

"You have caused me enough misery in my life. I will not allow it any longer. When I get home, I am going to tell my brother, Jerome, that you are threatening me. If you do anything now, you will regret it."

"Who's your big bad brother?"

"I told you, Jerome. He is twice your size."

The boy mumbled something unintelligible as he walked briskly on ahead of me and disappeared into the woods. I never ever saw him again. I was happy that he was no longer in school to harass Althea, who was now on her own.

CARS DIDN'T TRAVEL THAT ONE LANE ROAD VERY often, so the path was especially scary when dusk began to fall. Another young man tried to follow me on one occasion. I told him I was going to wait at the crossroads for my brother, and if he were present when Jerome came, it would be too bad for him. He went on ahead of me, and I ran the remainder of the way home.

Encounters with lone young men happened frequently and I became concerned about my safety. I used the threat of my older brother many times but realized it was dangerous for me to be on that deserted road alone. I armed myself with a sharp knife. Thank God I never had to use it.

After learning most of the operations at the silk mill, I was given a job in the soaking room. Silk was tied in bundles, dyed in large vats, and dried, first in a huge dryer, and then placed on racks. Afterward, the silk was sent to the girls who worked the machines.

Two of us worked in the soaking room. The other girl, named Alma, and I reported to our supervisor who oversaw the soaking and dyeing operation. His last name was Hiller, but Alma called him Brother Hiller. He was always happy, upbeat, and different from other men I knew in my life. I got an early impression that he knew everything I was thinking. He often talked about God to anyone who would listen. As I heard his words, I began to experience unfamiliar feelings and blushed when he looked my way. I was very uncomfortable and considered looking for another job.

One day, Alma didn't come to work, and I knew I'd have to talk to the supervisor. He whistled a tune I thought I knew.

"I bet I know what you're whistling."

Seemingly surprised that I spoke, he said, "Oh yeah, what is it?"

I said, "Isn't it Here We Gather Every Morning?"

"No,' he said, it's "What a Friend We Have in Jesus." Then he added,

"Do you know Him?"

I stammered something, not knowing for sure what he meant. Then he said, "You can know Him if you really want to."

"How?" I asked, "I pray to God and Jesus all the time, but I don't think God is interested in someone as insignificant as me. He has the whole world to look after, and I'm not sure He has time to hear my little voice."

Brother Hiller said, "All you have to do is talk to Him and ask Him to save your soul."

I pondered what he had told me for many days.

Brother Hiller frequently asked me, "Have you settled it? Have you asked Him?"

"How can I talk to God?"

He replied, "Just like you're talking to me. He'll hear you."

I went to the mill for work on Labor Day, not knowing it was closed. When I arrived, I saw the sign on the door "Closed for Labor Day". After walking all that distance, I was ashamed that anyone would find out I was unaware that Labor Day was a holiday. I didn't want anyone to see me, so I decided not to walk the road home. Instead, I planned to walk through the village that led to the railroad tracks. The tracks ran parallel below our road on the way to our farm. But in my spirit, I was very troubled. I wanted to become a Christian. I needed to experience the peace and joy I saw evident in Brother Hiller.

I started through the woods. After a few steps, I fell to my knees and began to cry as I told God I didn't know how to talk to Him. Then God said to me, "Remember when you were only eight years old? You knew how to talk to me then, and I heard you."

I realized I was still that child just longing to be restored by God's grace. How wonderful it was to know my prayers at eight years old were pleasing to God and connected me to Him even now.

The next day when I saw Brother Hiller, He asked, "Have you talked with God? Do you know His son, Jesus?"

I said, "I think I'm saved, but I'm still not sure."

"Well, if there was a dance you could attend on one corner of the town, and a church service on another corner, where would you go?"

I said, "I would go to church."

"Then you're saved," he said.

I just needed him to tell me that. Joy filled my heart and through the remainder of my life, through a world of trouble, I have always been able to find God's joy.

Chapter Sixteen

FORGIVE

To say that my mother was unpredictable is an understatement. We never knew for certain where she was living or what she might be doing. Out of the blue, she showed up one day at our house. She was on her best behavior, and we were getting along well as a family. But after a few weeks, she and Papa began to argue daily, and he started drinking again, making their relationship more difficult than ever.

I decided to get an apartment in Holmesdale for Mother and me. I had hopes of helping her live a respectable life for a change, wishing she could still find some decency and peace in herself. Everything was arranged for us to move into the apartment when she decided to take a brief trip to Scranton. I hoped she would not tell her disreputable friends where we were planning to move. She was gone for more than three weeks.

Meanwhile, I informed the landlord that I was unable take the apartment until I knew my mother's intensions. By the time she returned home, the apartment was rented to someone else. I vowed that I was through trying to help her.

She cried and told me she didn't have any means of coming back to see us. I had learned not to trust or believe her because she was always able to find her way to Scranton. I thought that if she really wanted to come home, she could arrange transportation.

"I don't care what happens to you any longer, Mother. You are your own worst enemy, and I give up hoping you will ever change."

She left the room and did not speak to me again for several days. That was well enough for me because her silence meant we were not arguing.

Mother stayed for a few more weeks. After she left home again, we seldom saw her. She returned home on some holidays and at other times when the notion suited her. By then, Loretta, at seventeen, got pregnant and had a beautiful baby boy, named Bobby. When Mother learned she was a grandmother, she returned home and took charge of the baby and our lives. She attempted to control me as if she had never left home, but I refused to accept her authority. I believed she had forfeited the right to tell me what to do. Her interference in our lives, only when it suited her, infuriated me.

Living as a Christian and showing patience and love for my family required me to pray constantly for God's guidance and help. All the problems that surrounded me made it difficult to live as a child of God. In one of my desperate moments, I told Brother Hiller about my life at home. Although I had not discussed much of my family problems, I am sure he already had an idea about how things were before we spoke. My mother's reputation was no secret in White Mills, and my father's drinking problems were well known by all who knew him.

I spoke through tears. "Sometimes my heart is filled with disgust for my parents, especially Mother. Just when I believe she will do what is right, she brings more shame to our family. And Papa, I love him, but he can be so cruel when he drinks."

"Have you prayed for them?"

"Every day," I said, "but I think God has given up on them."

"God hasn't given up on them, but have you, Sister Anna?"

"No, but I don't know what else to do."

"You must forgive your parents, Anna. That is the only way you will find peace with God."

I mulled his words over and over. Papa, I could forgive even though he had given me many anxious moments and inflicted real pain on me as a child. At least, he had expressed regret to me during those days when we worked together in the field. But it would be harder to forgive my mother. She was unyielding and never expressed regret for any pain or shame she caused our family.

Brother Hiller told me, "You must pray about it. God will lead you to forgiveness."

I decided I would do my best to have a good relationship with my mother. After a week or two, Mother and I were speaking kindly to each other again, and I was happy to think she might stay with us so we could have a normal family. Just when things were going well, Mother's demons reappeared. They were evident in her obvious contempt for

Papa and the indiscretion with which she spoke of other men in her life.

I feared that Loretta was following in our mother's footsteps. She often went to dances or the movies, leaving me to care for Bobby, my little nephew. Usually, she didn't return until the early morning hours. I couldn't sleep well when the baby was fretful.

Mother returned to live in Scranton but decided to come home for a few days. She slept in a bed across the room from the baby and me. Bobby was crying continuously. I tried to feed him the bottle Loretta prepared for him before she left for the evening, but he wouldn't drink it. He wouldn't stop crying, and Mother began to complain because she could not sleep.

"Can't you shut him up? Every time I close my eyes, he starts screaming."

"I'm trying, Mother," I said, "but I'm afraid something is wrong with him."

"Yes, something is wrong with him; he is spoiled rotten. Where is that damned Loretta?"

"She won't be home for a while. I'll make him stop crying."

I lifted Bobby from the bed and held him on my shoulder while I walked back and forth across the room. After a few minutes, he was quiet. I was tired and had to get up at five a.m. to get ready for work, so I laid him on the bed. As soon as I did, he screamed louder than before.

"Shut that little monster up, or I will."

Mother jumped from her bed and ran toward the baby. I threw my body over Bobby to shield him. She vented her anger by pounding me on the back with her fists. I did not make a sound or cry out; there was no way I would give her satisfaction by letting her know she hurt me. She mumbled hateful words as she went back to her bed and lay down. It was then I believed I could never forgive my mother, even if it displeased God. I would never attempt to have a good relationship with her again.

I checked the baby's bottle and discovered the milk was thick and spoiled. After making him a new bottle, he went to sleep, but I could not. When Loretta returned, I had difficulty sleeping, so I took a flashlight and a book of Bible meditations and walked up a hill where I knelt before God. He spoke to me through the meditations. It was beautiful. I wept and laughed and praised God. When I came down from the hill before daybreak, my joy was complete. God gave me His forgiveness as I forgave others, even my mother, whom I had vowed never to forgive.

I prayed so many prayers for my sister, Loretta, and they did not go unanswered. She became a kind and caring person. She often asked me to pray for her and for others she knew. Once, she asked me to visit an old lady, Mrs. Welch, who was quite sick, and I agreed. I told Mrs. Welch I would be praying for her. She became hostile when she learned of my mission and asked me to leave, saying, "I don't want your prayers. How can you be so presumptuous? I can pray for myself if I need to. I will be praying for you too. It won't hurt."

After a few weeks, Loretta asked me to visit the old lady again. I was reluctant, but God said go. I was trembling when I heard her calling for me to come in. She was unable to walk to the door.

She reached for my hand and held it warmly between hers. "Thank you, honey, for caring enough to come back. It is a

wonder you did after the way I resisted your efforts to be kind
to me. After you left, I kept thinking how good it was of you to
pray for me. I called my minister to tell him what had
happened. He told me we all pray to the same God and that I
should be thankful for your prayers." Then she added, "Don't
you ever let anyone turn you away from God, not me or anyone
else."

I was so happy He made me go back!

As I opened the door to leave, she said, "I want you to pray
for my nephew, Anthony."

"Anthony?"

"Yes," she said, "Anthony Miller. He's a mean boy. They
tell me his young brother-in-law, only fifteen, shot him last
week."

"Is he dead?'

"No, but he is in bad condition."

"I'll pray for him." But I wondered if I could humble
myself before God to pray for someone as evil as Anthony,
someone whose name I did not wish to have on my tongue.

Chapter Seventeen

THROUGH THE WOODS

As I walked through the woods on the way home, I felt the presence of God. I fell to my knees and prayed. I thought of Mrs. Welch's request that I pray for her nephew, Anthony. It was my obligation, as a Christian, to pray for all lost souls, even the man I had hated for the past three years. He caused the death of my dearest sister and her unborn baby. I could not wish him well, but I asked God to forgive Anthony if he should repent before Him. I never knew whether God answered my prayer or if Anthony asked Him for forgiveness.

I thought it best to keep news of Anthony's shooting to myself. However, it would be difficult because I knew Jerome would be happy to hear about it. I prayed for guidance as I continued my walk home. God let me know that Jerome should be told because no one mourned Margie's death more than he did. I thought he would find some solace in knowing Anthony had paid for being so evil. But Jerome had already heard about the shooting. The news of it revived his hatred for our former brother-in-law. There would be no sorrow in Jerome's heart for Anthony.

"I heard about his shooting this morning when I went to Scranton. He was beating his wife, and her brother shot him. Too bad it didn't kill him."

"May God forgive you, Jerome, for saying that," my father said.

But Jerome replied, "May God let Anthony suffer the way Margie did. I would go put him out of his misery myself if I knew where he was."

I pondered Jerome's words, hoping he didn't mean them but fearing he did. I said, 'If he doesn't repent, God will make him suffer. You won't have to do anything, brother."

That evening, we shared the news about Anthony around our supper table. Ralph shouted "halleluiah" before putting a spoonful of soup into his mouth. Papa said something about the man getting what he deserved. Tears filled Jerome's eyes as he got up from the table and left the room. I silently prayed for God to deliver us from evil. When supper was over, we all seemed deflated, each of us mourning Margie again in our own subdued ways. I was happy Anthony was no longer a part of our lives, and yet he was; he would be as long as we held memories of our Margie and how she died.

Shortly after, I began attending cottage prayer meetings in nearby Christian homes. The meetings often ended after dark —meaning I had to walk home on a wooded road. Although I was concerned about my safety along the trail, I would not miss an opportunity to worship and testify with my fellow believers. As I listened to the testimonies each week, my faith manifested itself in my own testimony. The faith of others who had survived difficulties in life gave me strength, and I grew in the Lord. Sometimes, I brought friends from town home with me for worship—to the consternation of my family. My siblings, and even my father, showed their disapproval by making distracting sounds from an adjacent room. Still, I persisted, growing stronger in my faith each day. I often visited the sick and infirm and prayed with them in their homes, taking the trail through the woods on the way back.

On one occasion, as I walked home from Honesdale, the sky darkened quickly. I felt unusually vulnerable. It was four miles to my house and would take me at least an hour and a half, even if I walked as fast as I could. I was still small for my age and had no means of protection since I had disposed of the knife I once carried. My only shield was my Lord and Savior, who always watched over me and on whom I leaned constantly. I shivered in the cool of the October evening and pulled my light jacket collar up close to my ears, and hurried along the rocky trail I knew well, even in the fading light.

Behind me, I heard a twig break and steps coming toward me. I hurried my pace, afraid to look back. The steps behind me quickened and grew louder. I could no longer resist looking over my shoulder, still walking as fast as my legs would go. A huge man—I couldn't see his face—now ran toward me. I ran too, but I realized I would soon be at the mercy of this dark hulk.

His grunts and heavy breathing told me he was only a few feet behind me. I was tired and ready for whatever might come next. The Twenty-Third Psalm ran through my mind. I stopped and turned toward the man. His huge hand reached for me, and I could smell whiskey in the deep breaths he exhaled. I opened my arms in the form of a cross, my small body trembling.

"May God have mercy on your soul." My cry shattered the stillness of the evening.

"Damn, girl, who are you?"

"A child of God, a disciple of Jesus."

The man's eyes widened. He released his hold on my jacket. His head shook from side to side, then he turned and ran back in the direction from which he came.

I fell to my knees and thanked Jesus, grateful he had traveled that path through the woods with me and would travel every other perilous path I would take through my troubled but blessed life.

I learned later that this man lived in one of the houses I passed every time I walked that wooded trail. No doubt, he waited along the road for me to appear. Fortunately, his intentions became clear, I felt God's power, and my fears disappeared. That is how it is when you accept God and His son, Jesus, as your protectors.

Later, I learned the man had a history of child abuse and an unscrupulous reputation. It was alleged that he ruined the lives of several young girls while working as a janitor in one of the nearby schools. I thanked God again for safely bringing me through the woods that night and saving me from that evil man. For if we trust in God, He will not forsake us. My life has been a testament to that.

I was late for supper that evening, but Loretta set aside a plate of potatoes and hominy for me. She sat at the table while I ate.

"I visited Mrs. Welch this morning. She would be very grateful if you would come to pray with her again."

"Is it about Anthony?"

"I think so," she said. "He is in constant pain from the gunshot lodged in his neck. He can't walk."

"She wants me to pray for him?"

"I think so."

"I'll think about it, Sister; maybe he is just paying for his sins."

I asked God for guidance when I knelt to pray before getting into bed. I fell into a troubled sleep, waking up after midnight with Anthony on my mind. I prayed for Jesus to tell me what to do but found no answers to my prayers. I knew the vengeance I felt in my heart was an awful sin, but I fell asleep again, expecting something terrible to come to Anthony. I was at peace with those thoughts. There would be no prayers for him by me that night.

Chapter Eighteen

I was a pretty girl when I was sixteen, and many people told me so. My father had grown very fond of me and often insisted that I play the piano and sing for his friends. He would proudly announce that I acquired my musical talents from him. Since his playing always caused him much pain, and he had difficulty standing, he used my playing and singing abilities to demonstrate his own talents by proxy.

After his friends left for the evening, I would let Papa know I did not like performing in front of all his guests, especially when they had been drinking.

"I'm proud of you, Anna, and want to show you off," he would say.

And although I was happy that he appreciated my talents, I was not comfortable being in a room with only older men. Papa would tell me, "Just sing whatever you want. Sing about Jesus if that makes you happy."

Even though I ministered to my family, Jerome and Ralph had not forgotten about the heresy of Reverend

Castaldo and continued to make atheistic pronouncements. And Papa was still angry at God for all his past troubles but sometimes asked for His blessings. I offered to turn the pages while he read the Bible, but he never acquiesced. I held out hope for his return to God and the conversion of my two brothers, both now in their twenties. So, when Father asked me to play and sing, I overcame my reluctance and performed, hoping it might help bring all my family and my father's friends unto God.

They often would weep when I played, but I never knew if it was because they appreciated the messages in my songs or because they were drinking so much. I received such peace from the beautiful gospel songs I sang, even if they did not.

These same friends of my father attended the dances where he played the accordion. Since I had become very good at square dancing, I enjoyed these opportunities to be with friends who accepted us despite the sullied reputation of my family. My father often demanded that I do the Charleston and polka, which I was also quite good at. But I did not believe that it was appropriate in front of so many people. I danced because Papa insisted, but I hated it.

Once, we had a house party and invited several friends. Papa asked me to play my accordion and sing for our guests. I rejoiced in the words of "The Old Rugged Cross," which I sang enthusiastically. The next morning, Papa told me I had embarrassed him and his guests by singing such a deeply religious song since many of his friends did not believe in God. I did not understand his displeasure since I had sung songs of faith for his friends in the past.

"Why didn't you sing Barbara Allen? You do it so well."

"I thought they would enjoy the gospel songs. Your friends always seem to like them."

"It's all right, Anna. I won't ask you to play again."

And he didn't for a while. I learned from that experience that walking the Christian pathway was going to be challenging. I vowed to try to understand other people's weaknesses as well as my own. God had much work to do in me so I could show more love to other people, especially my parents. You have heard me say before that God works in mysterious ways, and He had everything planned and gave me an opportunity to show that love for my father in a surprising way.

I was laid off from work for two weeks. On my first day without working, Papa came home very late. I heard the horse and buggy pull up to the front porch and expected him to come into the house where his supper was waiting. After a few minutes, I went outside to check on him. He was still in the buggy and was groaning with pain.

I shined a flashlight into his face and cringed when I saw blood trickling from a huge gash on his forehead. Another cut over his ear dripped onto his shoulder. My first instinct was to believe Papa was too drunk to walk and had fallen attempting to get onto his wagon. In his barely conscious state, he was not aware of his surroundings or how he had gotten home. I could tell by the deep scratches and scrapes on his hands that he had been in a struggle with someone.

I climbed onto the buggy alongside him and asked what had happened. He mumbled barely intelligible words, but he was able to tell me that Anthony's brother, Robert, had attacked him. Robert accused Papa of planning the shooting of Anthony and encouraging Jerome to kill him.

In the days that followed, Papa's recollection of the events of that evening appeared to return. He recalled that Robert vehemently accused Jerome of being his brother's assailant. Papa said he told Robert, "Jerome is a better shot than that; if he were the one who attacked Anthony, he would be a dead man, not just injured."

According to Papa, Robert became irate and struck him across his ear with a shovel. While Papa was lying on the ground, Robert kicked him on his forehead. Papa fought back but was a little intoxicated. "Besides," he said, "Robert is a humongous man like his brother."

As Robert rode away on his horse, he yelled at Papa, "You tell that son of yours I'm coming after him. Nothing else better happen to my brother."

Papa's attacker left him beaten and bleeding by the railroad tracks, where he lay moaning for at least an hour. A Good Samaritan heard his cries and came to his rescue. He helped Dad back onto his buggy, and Jasper brought him home. Father was barely aware of where the horse was taking him. I thank God that Jasper knew his way.

I assured Papa he was safe. Using all my strength, I helped him down from the buggy. I woke Ralph. Together, we assisted Papa upstairs and to bed. After helping him to bed, Ralph took care of the horse. I considered waking Jerome, but I knew he would not accept the attack on Papa as calmly as Ralph did. If he knew what happened, Jerome would be on his way before morning to avenge our father, and that would only have made matters worse. There would be plenty of time to confront

Robert. But I knew Jerome would not allow him to go unpunished for harming Papa.

THE NEXT DAY, WE DETERMINED THAT PAPA HAD several cracked ribs from being kicked. He developed pneumonia and almost died. I spent my time off from work taking care of him as well as I could. I prayed that Father would accept Christ again, but he did not. However, it wasn't long before I perceived a change in his attitude and that of Jerome. They were two prideful people who hated to admit any wrong in their lives. But slowly, *God* and *Christ* returned to their everyday vocabulary, giving me hope they would soon profess a belief in my Lord and Savior.

Papa slowly recuperated, and I went back to work at the silk factory. After work, I loved to talk about Christ with my fellow employees and new friends. At first, they accepted me, but when they learned about my family's reputation, many explained that they could no longer be my friend. When given the opportunity, I let them know I would keep them in my prayers, and I forgave them for their blindness. But praise God, I was given a new family in the Assembly of God Church, and I loved those members as much as my own flesh and blood. I found solace in their company and began spending more time away from home and among my Christian friends.

When Jerome learned that Anthony's brother was the man who beat our father almost to death, he vowed to get even with Robert and Anthony, not only for Papa's injuries but also for our sister, Margie, who was beaten to death by Anthony.

I feared what might happen next.

Chapter Nineteen

MIRACLES

I believe in miracles because so many have occurred in my life, some minor but startling; others changed me in distinct and unmistakable ways. I have no explanation for how I survived a plane ride in a two-seater open biplane without a seat belt, but I did.

By the time I was sixteen, single and two-lane macadam roads were built in rural Pennsylvania near the cities, including Scranton. It was common to see cars and small trucks on those roads. By 1935 airplanes were frequenting the skies. When they flew over our farm, we ran outside and pointed upward to the planes. My heart leaped with excitement when one of the planes flew low enough for us to see the pilot, wearing his goggles and cap buckled under his chin.

I tugged at Jerome's arm. "I would give anything to go on a plane ride."

"You wouldn't be scared?"

"No," I told him. "I would just be a little closer to God."

My seventeenth birthday was a few weeks away. You can

imagine my surprise when, the night before, Jerome told me that he and Loretta had arranged for me to go to Scranton and fly in one of those planes. The flight lasted only thirty minutes from takeoff to landing. Still, it was the greatest thrill I ever experienced other than being saved by Jesus Christ. Soaring above all the problems I experienced down on earth, I was excited to see our farm below me, and I thanked God that Loretta and Jerome loved me enough to give me such a gift for my birthday.

"Hang on," the pilot yelled back at me moments before he flipped the plane upside down. We flew that way for a minute or more. I was a little scared, watching the earth come rushing toward us, and then I breathed a sigh of relief as the pilot gently set the plane onto the ground.

When he killed the engine, he said over his shoulder. "You can undo your seatbelt now."

"What seatbelt?" It was then I realized I was sitting on the two ends of the belt.

"My God, girl, I don't know why I didn't lose you. Angels must be watching over you."

"They are," I said.

I trembled a little after I was back on the ground, realizing I had not understood what the pilot meant when he told me to buckle up before the plane took off. That adventure convinced me more than ever that my life was in God's hands and He had plans for me.

In the Bible books of Mathew, Mark, and John, we are told that Jesus walked on water after feeding a throng of five thousand with five loaves of bread and two fish. He healed the sick and the lame and gave sight back to the blind. If Jesus could do that, surely, He still performs miracles in our lives when we call on Him.

As I prepared for a cottage prayer meeting at the home of a fellow believer, I listened to the Carter Family singing "Will the Circle Be Unbroken," and my heart was filled with gratitude to my Lord and Savior. When the time came for me to leave for the meeting, dark clouds rolled over our house, and thunder could be heard in the distance. I was consumed with a deep feeling of faith. Savoring the words of the song I had just heard, I opened the door to leave, and the wind blew it shut.

Papa asked, "Where do you think you are going in this weather? It's about to storm."

"To the prayer meeting."

"Only a fool would go out on a night like this."

"A fool or a true believer, Papa," I said, then passed by his chair and kissed him on the forehead.

I opened the door again. The wind had stopped blowing, and the thunder had quieted.

I started out walking fast. About halfway to the village, giant raindrops began to fall on the leaves of the trees. I took shelter under a large oak and asked the Lord to please hold back the rain until I could get to Brother Gregory's house, where the meeting was. being held. The rain stopped, and I continued on, arriving in time to worship with my friends.

During the meeting, we could hear the relentless rain falling outside. Our singing and praise drowned out the storm, but I was aware of the conditions I would face on my return home.

After the meeting, Brother Gregory said, "Anna, you'll have to stay with us tonight. It's raining so hard out there."

I said, "Brother Gregory, let's all pray for the rain to stop until I get home. God kept me dry on my way here, and I believe he will stop the rain until I get home if we call on His name. I was not attempting to appear sanctimonious, but I wanted to demonstrate my deep faith in Jesus Christ, my Lord and Savior."

I imagined my request tested the faith of all who attended the meeting, but I was confident in the power of prayer.

Brother Gregory pointed to the roof. "Hear that rain?"

I remembered what Jesus said to Peter when He attempted to walk toward Jesus, "O, ye of little faith," and I knew the rain would stop if I asked.

"It can't be raining, Brother Gregory, because I asked God to keep me from getting wet on the way home."

He went to the door and opened it. "Come see for yourself."

I did as he asked. From the doorway, I could see the sky full of bright shining stars. I shouted. "Hallelujah! Praise God, for he is good."

I walked the three miles home under the stars, thanking God all the way. A few minutes after I arrived home, rain began to pelt our roof. I don't know if I ever felt more grateful to God than at that moment. I held my hands over my heart as I fell asleep.

Chapter Twenty

UNDER SUSPICION

The next morning, I awoke early, still feeling the glow from my prayer meeting the previous night. Shortly after I prepared to walk to my job at the silk mill in downtown White Mills, I heard a car pull up. There was a knock on our door. I was surprised to see Sheriff Millard Langford, who sometimes attended our prayer meetings, standing on our front porch.

"Hello, Sheriff," I said, "What are you doing out this way so early?"

"Well, Anna." The sheriff hesitated for a moment, then continued, "I am really sorry about this, but I need to talk to your brothers about some trouble they might be involved in."

"Jerome and Ralph?"

"Really, just Jerome, but Ralph may be helpful if he is around."

"Ralph isn't home and hasn't been for almost a week. He stays in Scranton most of the time. He and his band play at a place called Country Time Parlor. I think that is a fancy name for a nightclub."

"How about Jerome? Is he home?"

"Can you tell me what it's about?"

"I'd rather not until I speak with him."

I can't explain where my courage came from, but I was determined not to wake up Jerome until I knew why the sheriff wanted to speak with him. "Brother Millard, I won't let you talk to him until you tell me what it is about."

His frustration was showing. He took off his hat and wiped his brow with his forearm. "You are one stubborn woman, Sister Anna."

"Not stubborn, just determined."

"I hate to tell you that Anthony Miller was found dead alongside the road into Orson this morning. Nobody knows how he got there because he couldn't walk on his own."

"Why do you think my brothers had something to do with it?"

"Well, Sister Anna, I've been told, and I understand that Jerome harbored ill feelings toward Anthony and even threatened to kill him."

"My brother was just venting his anger. He couldn't kill a fly."

"Just the same, I need to talk with him if he will come with me voluntarily, and I will bring him back home after we talk."

I went upstairs and aroused Jerome. "Anthony has been killed, and the sheriff wants to talk to you about it. I know you couldn't have done it because you were home all night."

"I don't know anything about that. I'm sure as hell not

unhappy about it, but I didn't kill him. I hope that whoever did it is never caught."

"It might be good if you talk with Sheriff Langford. He's a good man." I assured my brother that the sheriff was just trying to quell any rumors about Anthony's death.

I waited while Jerome got dressed. He came onto the porch and shook hands with the sheriff. They moved out of my earshot and talked. After a few minutes, Jerome told me he was going with the sheriff to White Mills.

"If you are ready, he will give you a ride into town. There's no use in you walking."

Jerome did not appear nervous or concerned as he rode in the front seat next to Sheriff Langford, but my heart was pounding. I repeated The Twenty-Third Psalm over and over and prayed silently that my brother was not guilty of killing Anthony.

The day passed slowly for me, and as I walked through the woods on my way home, I prayed for Jerome. It was an hour before sunset, and rays of sunlight showed through the leaves. I could see Jesus in the rays. A halo was about his head.

He said to me, "Don't worry, Anna, for I will take care of your brother." My burdens became lighter, and I quickened my pace toward home.

I reached our house at dusk. Jerome was sitting in a rocking chair on the front porch. He smiled broadly and hugged me when I reached the top step.

"Don't look so sad, Anna. We don't have anything to worry about. The sheriff thinks someone drove Anthony out on the roadway and dumped him. Since I don't have a car and don't know anyone who does, I am not suspected of harming him."

"Do they know how he died?"

"Sheriff says he may have to send Anthony's body to Scranton for an autopsy. Our coroner isn't qualified to do them."

"Poor Anthony," I said. "It must be awful to be hated like he was."

"Poor Anthony? Poor Margie, I say. He killed her and the baby, didn't he? And he deserved whatever happened to him."

I DON'T REMEMBER HOW LONG IT WAS, BUT AT LEAST two weeks before we heard anything else about Anthony's death. When we did, everyone in my family was relieved, especially Jerome.

On a trip into the city, he bought a copy of *The Tribune*, a newspaper from Scranton. The paper contained a story at the bottom of the front page about a suspicious death. According to the paper, Anthony was left alongside a dirt road and died from exposure. The case was still being investigated at the time, and no one had been charged with his death.

Because Jerome was initially suspected, he wanted to know more about what really happened. He hitched up the wagon and drove to Orson to talk with Brenda Miller, Anthony's wife, and her fifteen-year-old brother, Jimmy. Brenda wouldn't talk to Jerome, but her brother did after Jerome told him about Anthony's cruelty to Margie.

"That's why I shot him in the first place," Jimmy said. "He

was beating Brenda for no reason, making things up just so he could have an excuse to hit her."

"I don't blame you for shooting the son-of-a-bitch. He deserved everything that happened to him.

"I'm just sorry I didn't kill him."

"Who did then?"

"I can't say anymore. If Robert learns that I did it, he will kill me and my sister."

Jimmy stopped talking for a minute, but Jerome wanted to know more. "Have you been accused of shooting him?"

"No." He shook his head. "I'm just a kid. No one thinks I did anything wrong ."

"The sheriff won't ever hear it from me, but how did he end up alongside the road?"

"I'm not afraid of ever being arrested for shooting him," the young boy said, "because it was in self-defense. Anthony turned on me when I tried to stop him from hurting my sister. He threatened to kill me, and he was big enough to do it if I didn't shoot him. Everybody knows that."

"Wasn't Anthony staying with your sister after he was shot?"

"Yes. But he was helpless and couldn't stand on his feet; couldn't even feed himself."

"How did he end up alongside the road?"

The boy appeared reluctant to tell the story of Anthony's death. But Jerome wanted to know how Anthony died. He coaxed Jimmy, promising never to tell anyone else about it.

According to Jimmy, Anthony experienced an unusual amount of pain that evening, much more than usual. He screamed and begged for help. Brenda drove to the adjacent town to fetch a doctor, but he was already on an emergency call. When she returned, the three of them decided to put Anthony onto the back of the old flatbed truck and take him to Scranton for help. Since he couldn't get out of bed or stand, Brenda, Jimmy, and their mother loaded him into a wheelchair and moved him onto the front porch. Jimmy backed the truck next to the porch, and the three of them rolled him onto the back of the truck. Jimmy sat alongside Anthony as they drove toward Scranton.

About two miles down the muddy road, the truck became stuck in ruts. Efforts to get it moving failed. Because Anthony weighed nearly three-hundred pounds, Jimmy suggested the arduous task of lifting Anthony from the truck to lighten the load and then somehow putting him back onto the truck. During their attempts to lower him to the ground, Anthony fell, hitting his head. They pushed for several minutes to free the truck. By the time it was out of the mud, the three of them were exhausted. They waited for someone to come along and help, but it got very dark on the country road. Anthony was no longer making a sound and appeared not to be breathing. They feared he would die without a doctor's care. They moved him off the road. Jimmy stayed with him while Brenda and her mother drove to town for help. They were still unable to find a doctor, and when the two of them returned, Anthony was dead.

Jerome asked, "Have you told anyone else?"

"Yes, the sheriff. A few days later, he took the three of us into Scranton and questioned us for two hours. He decided we did nothing wrong and let us go."

"That must have been after he questioned me. I must have

been the first one they suspected. I'm not sorry the bastard is dead. He killed my sister."

"And he probably would have killed mine if I didn't shoot him."

Jerome gave Jimmy a reassuring pat on his shoulder. He promised the boy he would not tell anyone about their discussion. To my knowledge, I am the only person he has ever told. I never heard any more about Anthony's death, and as far as I know, nothing more was ever printed in *The Tribune*.

When I heard how Anthony died, I thought of Margie's suffering at his hands, all the times I heard her crying out in pain and begging him to stop beating her. I thought about what a good mother she would have been to her baby boy and how all of us who loved her were deprived of that. It would have been easy to hate Anthony at that moment, but God would not allow it in my heart. The thoughts and words did not come easy, but I struggled through prayer, asking the Lord to forgive Anthony for his sins.

Second Interlude

I read late into the night, eager to know more about this courageous and devout woman. With her frail, bent body, she measured no more than five feet tall, even on her best days. Hunched over her walker, she appeared smaller than that. However, character is not determined by physical size but by integrity, devotion to our principles, and love for God, country, and fellow man. In this regard, Anna Marie Gamble was a giant.

Even though I had nothing but admiration and love for her, I could not allay the feeling I was prying into secrets not intended to be revealed outside her family. For in her own words, she said, "I have not told the worst aspects of my family's life. There are things I prefer to remain unspoken, especially regarding my mother and father. I will always love them, no matter what, but it has not been easy to obey God's admonition to honor thy mother and father."

As I read more of Anna's memoir, I gleaned the essence of secrets written between her lines. In telling her story, I have tried not to insert my own facts. Still, I have gathered enough from what she wrote to understand the difficulties she experienced living amid the iniquities that continually surrounded her. Though she had justification for being ashamed of her mother and father, she never expressed that sentiment. My story of Anna takes the liberty to interpret this aspect of her life for my readers. Regardless of the problems that surrounded her, like Saint Bernadette, she remained faithful in her beliefs.

These thoughts made me recall the parallels that existed between Anna Marie Gamble and Bernadette Soubirous. Several years ago, I read the story of the peasant girl of Lourdes in France, who was canonized as a saint in the Catholic Church after her death. Bernadette lived her life of thirty-two years in the middle of the nineteenth century, and her story commences in 1858 with her vision of Our Lady of Lourdes. Franz Werfel relied on church records and tales and legends of the townspeople of Lourdes to author the story, *The Song of Bernadette*, in 1941. I am fortunate to have Anna's own words that tell her story, not mine. She will never be canonized as a saint and would never have assumed that she warranted such an honor, but she truly lived a saintly life.

Her story continues...

Chapter Twenty-One

WHERE IS MOTHER?

It is strange how Anthony's death affected all of us. We discussed it around our dinner table the few times we sat as a family to eat. I think the events, as we understood them, brought back the poignancy of Margie's death and the terrible life she lived as Anthony's wife. Still, there was a sense of pity for the way he died, as voiced by my father.

"No one should have to die that way."

Jerome spoke up. "No, it should have been much worse. After the way he tormented Margie and his new wife, he should have been beaten the same way."

"Judge not, lest ye be judged," Papa responded. Perhaps his words revealed his problems over the years of dealing with his explosive temper and the times he had inflicted pain on his children and his own wife. Although such behavior by him was infrequent, nevertheless, it left an enduring reminder that he also possessed a cruel side.

Jerome pushed back his chair from the table. "The Bible

also talks about an eye for an eye and a tooth for a tooth, and that is what I believe."

As for me, as much as I had hated and feared Anthony when I was a child, the Word of God told me to forgive him. After those conversations, I would leave the dinner table, happy that Margie was in Heaven, no longer tormented by the cruel world in which we all still toiled and labored. Although our situation had improved since I was younger, my family was in disarray in many ways.

Mother had been gone for months with no communications of any kind. For all we knew, she might be dead. Loretta, then twenty-one, was pregnant for a second time by a man who promised to marry her but left her to fend for herself during her pregnancy. Althea, who was four years younger than I, had grown more erratic and difficult to deal with. She still had trouble walking and was possessed with an uncontrollable temper. She was brilliant in many ways, but because of her unruly behavior, she was expelled from school. Father was then faced with the task of finding a state institution for the mentally impaired to which he could send her. Poor Jerome had no life of his own, shouldering the responsibility for most of the farming and working odd jobs to keep our family fed and the rent on the farm paid.

If anyone of us was living a comfortable life, the way we wished to live it, that was Ralph. His dance band gained popularity in Scranton and eventually in small towns around the county. He needed a place for his band to practice. Since we had a large unused room, Ralph decided he would practice there, but the room was in poor condition. He agreed I could hold prayer meetings there if I would help him put up the wallpaper. The next day, Ralph bought the paper, and we worked for two days to complete the job. I made plans to volunteer the room for a cottage prayer meeting the next time I met with my Christian friends.

Jerome, who worked full-time on our farm in the summer, was a talented musician in his own right. He played the guitar, piano, accordion, and violin. When Ralph's violin player failed to show up one evening, Jerome filled in. Before long, he decided to go on the road with Ralph. Papa was not pleased with his decision, but Jerome was twenty-eight years old and had devoted most of his life working for our family because of Papa's poor health and crippled feet. It was time for Jerome to live his own life.

"Don't worry, Papa," Jerome said. "I will stay until the potatoes and corn are harvested, and I will come back once a week to check on things. When we are not playing, I will be here with you at home."

Papa replied, "I don't know what I will do without you here. Don't know how we will make it."

Our father was not a selfish man, but he could no longer do many of the physical tasks he once did before his arsenic poisoning. He had always depended on Jerome for help. I think he had never considered being left at home with three girls and no man to do manual work. That realization must have worried him. I was approaching eighteen, and he knew I was strong-willed and would not spend much time at home because of my job and church activity. Loretta was in her sixth month of pregnancy. She already had Bobby, who was five, and she would soon have another baby to care for. She was in no condition to help our father with any of the farm or household chores. Althea could not be depended on to do anything constructive. All these factors must have made Jerome's decision to go on the road with Ralph very difficult for Papa to accept.

"It will be fine," Jerome said. "Ralph and I will send you some money to help out. I won't be leaving for two or three weeks, but it's something I really want to do." He put his arms about Papa and held him close for several seconds.

Tears ran down Papa's face. He hugged Jerome, clinging to him until his eldest son moved away, wiping tears from his own eyes. "I love you Papa, but you have to understand how much this means to me."

"I do." Papa turned and walked out of the living room, his shoulders shaking with grief.

Jerome looked about the room, his eyes moving from person to person. I think he was looking for approval from us.

"I'm sorry to hurt him," he said, "but if I don't do this now, maybe I won't ever get another chance."

Loretta spoke up. "You don't owe anyone an apology, brother. You deserve a life of your own, and we wish the best for you."

We all nodded in agreement, but I felt a sense of doom with the thought of not having our big brother at home with us.

TWO WEEKS LATER, RALPH'S BAND PRACTICED IN THE newly wallpapered room and every week thereafter. When I was not attending a prayer meeting, I would sit in the adjoining living room and listen to the music. The band was quite good, and I sang along if I was familiar with the song they played. Someone in the band heard me singing in the next room and suggested to Ralph that I should be part of the band. I sang a few times, but most of the music played by the band departed too far from my Christian beliefs. I stopped singing with the band; but Loretta, who loved dance music and was far more worldly than I, agreed to sing in local nightclubs after she delivered her new baby, but would not go on the road with the band.

The lead guitar player, whose name was Bennie Matthews, took an immediate liking to Loretta, and she happily returned his sentiments. He was nineteen, two years younger than Loretta, but that didn't prevent him from asking her to marry him after knowing each other for less than two months. Loretta delivered her baby girl, Lucy, a month later, to the delight of all of us. Bennie accepted the new baby and Bobby as his own, and he and Loretta married two weeks afterwards. I think all of us had reservations but dared not express them to Loretta. It remained to be seen just how the marriage would withstand weeks of separation when the band traveled.

November was unusually cold that year, and our house was only marginally heated, with a heating stove in the living room and a wood stove for cooking in the kitchen. I planned to hold a cottage prayer meeting in the room where the band practiced, but Papa said it was too cold, and that we would have to hold the meeting in the kitchen. The devotional was to take place on the following Saturday. Since Brother Randolph had a phone and could notify other members, I walked to his home to let him know I was ready to lead the next prayer meeting at my house.

That Friday, Ralph came home, driving a 1932 Ford Model
T, which he was in the process of buying. The roadway to our
house from the main road was a partially muddy and frozen
mess due to the wagon tracks made by our buggy. We heard the
car coming, and all ran out to see as it got closer to our front
porch. You can imagine how surprised and happy we were to
see Ralph behind the steering wheel. But our glee was short-
lived.

Ralph carried a rolled-up newspaper in his hand as he
walked into the house, straight to the kitchen table. There, he
unfolded the newspaper and spread it out for all of us to see.

The Tribune headline read: PROSTITUTION RING
BROKEN UP: MADAM ARRESTED.

Below the first paragraph was a picture of our mother.

Chapter Twenty-Two

GOD DOES NOT FORSAKE

The time was approaching for me to lead our group in the evening prayer service. The report of Mother's arrest left me with dread, fearing that one or more of my church family had seen the headline and my mother's picture on *The Tribune's* front page. Prior to this, my family and I lived with the recognition that we were considered undesirable people, what we would label today as "white trash." Althea and I had suffered insults and embarrassment by our classmates and even one of our teachers. So, I was unsure how I would handle any questions or comments pertaining to my mother's alleged crimes. The only thing I understood I could do was to pray about our situation and believe that God would tell me what to say should any such problem arise. The knowledge that He does not forsake believers gave me the strength to carry on.

When I reminded my family of the pending prayer meeting and invited all of them to attend, they all refused and warned me not to say anything bad about Mother or anything else that might discredit our family.

In my walk with God, I came to realize that some people profess a belief in Him because they fear His retribution. They don't understand that God and His son are benevolent and care for their children, all of them, sinners and saints alike. Papa was like many such people. After his numerous misfortunes and tumultuous marriage, he would no longer voice a belief in God. Although he never spoke of it, I believed he was holding onto a relationship with Him through me. That belief made my worship of God all the more important. I saw my devotion as a path to salvation for my family. So regardless of any misgivings I encountered, I was determined to hold prayer meetings in our home.

As the time approached for the prayer meeting, I began clearing papers and candles from the large kitchen table. Papa called from the adjacent room.

"Leave those papers where they are, Anna."

The copy of *The Tribune*, with Mother's picture, lay among several magazines and other newspapers. I moved everything to the middle of the table and covered the article about Mother with all the other papers and magazines. I trusted that God would keep the article about my mother hidden from view.

Just before dark, my fellow Christians came. There were probably twelve to fifteen people, as I recall. Led by Reverend Randolph, we gathered around our table, some seated, some standing. Reverend Randolph led us in prayer then we sang several songs before the Bible reading. As I prepared to read, I watched nervously as the pastor fingered the stack of newspapers and magazines. I was prepared to be truthful about my mother and our family if someone brought the article in *The Tribune* to the attention of our group.

I assumed Papa and my brothers and sisters were listening nervously from the living room. I took a harmonica from my pocket and played a favorite song of Papa's "This Train is Bound for Glory." I was hoping he would enjoy the song and not say something that would interrupt the meeting or embarrass me.

When I finished the song, I opened my Bible to Psalm 120 and began reading:

> *I will lift up mine eyes unto the hills from which cometh*
> *my help. My help cometh from the Lord. The Lord*
> *shall preserve thy going out and coming in from this*
> *day forward and even evermore.*

I testified that God answered prayers and used the example of how He held back the storm while I traveled to and from our prayer meeting the previous week. Afterward, I led the group in prayer, asking for blessings on all our families and forgiveness for our many sins. Our pastor said a brief prayer to end the service and thanked me for my hospitality. He stated that he hoped my father and other family members would participate in the next meeting in our home. Then I heard Papa angrily clear his throat in the adjacent room. I suppose he feared my response might bring discredit to our family.

How ironic, that he still attempted to be prideful after all the times my father had staggered from the downtown bar, cursed his horse, and even his children if one of us happened to be present at the time. And our mother's sinful behavior was, no doubt, known by people who knew us. Nevertheless, I loved Papa, and most of all, did not wish him to forbid me to hold prayer meetings in our home again.

To my surprise, after prayer was over, my pastor asked me to sign a paper, an application to attend Practical Bible School in Johnson City, New York.

What a wonderful surprise! My heart was filled with joy until I thought about not having finished high school.

"But Pastor, I only have an eighth-grade education."

The pastor touched my shoulder. "Anna, you are blessed by God. You know more about the Bible than any other one of us. As your pastor, I know I shouldn't tell you that, but it is so. God has a special mission for you, and He will be with you every step of the way in Bible school. I will see that you get admitted, and I know you will do the rest."

As my guests filed out of the room after our meeting, I showed a copy of the application to Papa.

"What does this mean?"

"I'll be going off to Bible college in February."

"No daughter of mine is going to be a missionary, running around the world. I won't have it."

"I'm not going to be a missionary, but if that is something I wanted to do, I would do it, Papa."

He drew back his hand, and I stepped close to him, my hands at my side.

"Go ahead, Papa, but it won't stop me. Nothing will."

"You know you will put me in my grave, Anna."

"No, I won't, but you will put yourself in your grave if you continue your drinking and don't return to Jesus."

Papa turned to leave the room. "Go on," he said, "the sooner the better. You are an ungrateful girl, leaving us when we need you so badly now that Jerome is gone most of the time."

"I love you, Papa, and I suppose I love Mother, but neither of you has been a good parent. Your children, all of us, have survived on our own determination. The only ones you have shown real affection for were Horton and Althea,"

"I have done the best I know how," Papa said.

"Maybe you have, but what we really wanted was to be loved by our parents."

The door closed behind Papa. As he left the room, Althea fell to the floor and rolled around, foaming at her mouth. I leaned over her and attempted to caress her forehead. She rose to her knees then clawed both my arms, leaving bloody scratches. I slapped her face, stood, and moved away.

"No more, Althea. You will never hurt me again."

I told myself not to worry. I would be gone for good in three months. God would be with me in my walk with Jesus.

Chapter Twenty-Three

UNFAIR LABOR PRACTICES

In the midst of the Great Depression in 1936, many people were out of work, and some families couldn't pay for food or afford a roof over their heads. I was fortunate to have an income of at least eight dollars each week if I worked every day. But just before Christmas that year, I learned that I was being underpaid, as were all of my fellow workers. The wage rates for all positions were posted on a bulletin board where all employees clocked in for their shifts. I had never bothered to check the pay scales until one of my fellow employees brought it to my attention. At my advertised pay rate, I should have been earning at least ten dollars each week. As I write this, ten dollars does not seem to be a very impressive wage, but two dollars more each week would have been monumental to my family since I shared my pay with them.

When I learned the truth, I called it to the attention of my supervisor, Brother Hiller. He cautioned me that the mill was barely making a profit and might close if the depression continued. He explained that the markets for the products we made were disappearing almost weekly. Despite various programs enacted by President Franklin Roosevelt and the Democrats, our country was slow to recover from the depression. The silk mill had survived only because of the unique products we produced.

"Be cautious, Sister Anna, and pray before you decide to do anything about it."

That night, I prayed to God for guidance. I trusted Brother Hiller without question. But realized he had been with the silk mill for a long time and did not want to jeopardize his job and those of other workers. They were just grateful to be employed under almost any conditions, even unfair ones.

I thought about the advice from Brother Hiller, which I knew was given in good faith. But I could not accept a situation where the company advertised and posted erroneous pay scales. I reasoned that if the company was in trouble and unable to pay the amounts posted, the managers should be truthful with employees and let us know why our pay was less than advertised.

These thoughts dominated my prayers for the next several days. Finally, I asked God, "What do you want me to do? What would Jesus do?"

Just asking the questions made me realize I needed to ponder the issue no longer. I thought of Jesus when he expelled the merchants from the temple and turned over the tables of the money changers. According to the Gospel of Mark, chapter eleven, the merchants charged exorbitant prices to customers and desecrated God's house.

I reasoned that if Jesus were an employee at the silk mill, he would not hesitate to confront management, at least, demanding that employees be told the truth. How could I do less if I were truly following Him in my walk with God? I would let Him use me to expose the fraud at the mill.

Now that I decided to take some action, I had no idea how to go about it. The next day during my lunch break, I went to the small library in town and checked out a book on labor union activities. Even though all of us at the silk mill were members of the International Ladies Garment Workers Union, we had never held a local meeting or discussed our rights. If not for the discrepancies in our pay at the mill, I might never have been aware of the ILGWU. As I read of the sacrifices and dedication of women who were instrumental in organizing workers in the union, I was humbled to think I might be following in their shoes. My great hope was that whatever I did would glorify my Lord and Savior.

That night at home, I sat at the kitchen table thinking of my next steps. Somehow, the pencil in my hand began to write, and words that I had never spoken before appeared on the sheet of notebook paper. I realized then that what I was attempting to do was acceptable to God.

I mailed the letter the following day, addressed to the ILGWU Committee in New York, and did my utmost to put the issues out of my mind while waiting for a response that might never come. I told no one, not even Brother Hiller, what I had done.

About two weeks after I mailed the letter, an unfamiliar man showed up at the mill. Word got around that he was an investigator responding to a letter written by one of the employees. The man's name was Julius Thornton. If he had any idea of my identity as the writer, he never revealed it to anyone that I know of.

Before Mr. Thornton's last day in our facility, a notice was posted that all workers would receive union-scale wages starting immediately and that backpay would be given to everyone for the past month's wages. Somehow, word must have gotten around that I was responsible for our new pay because I was showered with candy bars by my fellow workers.

I had only one regret about my actions. Our superintendent, who was really a genuinely nice man, was soon replaced by a man from Scranton. His name was John Miller, which made me wonder if he was kin to Anthony, the man who was so cruel to my precious sister, Margie. After a week or two, he called me into his office to tell me he had heard of my mother's arrest. I never understood why he wished to tell me that, except to let me know he had something to hold over me in case I caused any more trouble for the mill. Now, my hopes that I would be approved for Bible school soon and be able to quit the mill occupied my mind almost constantly.

As I prayed by my bedside that night, I reminded myself of Jesus in the Garden of Gethsemane before his execution. What dread he must have endured, knowing the fate that awaited him. What pain he suffered on the cross, and all for my salvation. How could I fear any man or allow a threat to be held over my head to interfere with my daily walk with God? I would not allow Mr. Miller to intimidate me. With Jesus by my side, I would fear no man.

I ended each night's prayer with the Twenty-Third Psalm, my sustenance all my life when I was in the valley of the shadow of death.

Chapter Twenty-Four
ALTHEA'S VACATION

Even today, I don't really know how to describe my father. He was the most complicated man I have ever known, talented and blessed in so many ways and cursed in others, it seemed. He could be as cruel as Satan and then as meek as a lamb. I think he loved all his children but had difficulty showing it at times. He seemed to love the ones of us who were vulnerable and needy in some way; Poor Horton, so fragile and helpless, was Papa's favorite. He died at four years of age, and Papa grieved for weeks. After Horton's passing, Papa turned his affection toward Althea, who was, as we all said, "not right."

Althea was home full-time after being expelled from school. At fourteen, she was taller than I and "strong as Sampson," as Father said. She was a voracious reader and especially liked sentimental love stories and dramatic detective mysteries. Her memory was flawless, and she never forgot a name or face. Her physical abnormalities still limited her mobility. She had not outgrown her tendency to rock back and forth before taking a step. As she grew older, her outbursts and temper tantrums became more intolerable. Papa and I were the only family members who could control her when she exhibited her outrage.

Since Horton's death, I was Althea's caretaker most of the time, pulling her to school and protecting her from our abusers. Since I had been working at the silk mill for three years, Althea did not receive my usual attention. Loretta, who was still living at home with Bobby and her new baby, cooked meals and took care of housekeeping chores except on weekends when I was home, but she refused to assist with Althea because of her unpredictable behavior. Responsibility for Althea fell to Papa. He talked to the family about sending her to a home for mentally ill people, but we all knew such a decision weighed heavily on his mind. For that reason, none of us brought up the subject for a long time, not even with each other. Althea appeared to be happy under Papa's care. This arrangement functioned well until one afternoon when Papa decided he needed to go into town and visit his friends at the bar.

I worked until five o'clock that evening. As I walked toward the edge of town on my way to the path through the woods, I saw Papa's horse and buggy standing in the churchyard. I realized he was inside the bar drinking and had probably lost track of time. I had never been inside a bar, and I approached the door with dread. Papa was seated at a table, his head resting on his arms. I shook him by his shoulders, and he rose from his chair with his fists raised. He dropped his hands when he saw my face.

"I'm sorry, Anna," he said. "Can you forgive your father?"

"Yes, I forgive you, Papa, but it isn't up to me. It's between you and God."

He shouted across the barroom to a man I assumed to be a drinking comrade. "This is my good daughter. She is not like her mother."

I helped him to his feet and whispered. "Hush, Papa. Don't bring more shame on yourself."

He shook loose from me and staggered toward the door. I followed as he made his way down the steps and across the street to the churchyard where Jasper and his wagon waited. He climbed up to the seat and called out to me, "You coming or are you walking?"

I got up beside him. Several times, Papa fell asleep while holding the reins during our trip home. About the third time, I took the reins and urged Jasper on. The horse knew the way as well as I did. I think he probably brought Papa home many times after he let go of the reins. As I recall, we never exchanged words at all. We rode all the way home without speaking.

It was dark when we arrived. Papa went to the barn to put Jasper away for the night. Loretta met me at the door. She was crying.

"It's Althea. We've had a terrible fight."

"What happened?"

"She attacked Bobby because he picked up one of her books. I heard him screaming from Althea's bedroom and ran to see what was happening. She bloodied his nose and was choking him."

"God forbid," I said, unable to comprehend Althea's actions. Loretta's arms were bleeding. "She do that?"

"Yeah, when I tried to pull her away from Bobby, she turned on me."

I went into Althea's bedroom. She was lying across her bed. When I entered the room, she sat up. "What's wrong with Bobby?"

"You know what you did, Sister. You should be ashamed."

She lay back across her bed, beating the cover with her fists. She screamed at the top of her lungs. Papa appeared at her bedroom door. "What's wrong with my baby girl?"

"Nothing important, Papa," I quipped. "She only tried to kill little Bobby over a book."

Papa sat on Althea's bed and helped her into a sitting position, her legs hanging over the side of the bed. He placed his arms about her shoulders and pushed back her disheveled hair away from her face. "There, there," he said, "everything will be all right."

He motioned with his hand for me to leave the room. I stood by the door listening to Papa as he placated Althea, telling her she was not at fault, that he would not allow anyone to hurt her.

Loretta came to the door and listened along with me. I could see the frustration in her face. After a few minutes, she opened the door and stepped inside Althea's room.

"Papa, we have had enough of you protecting Althea. She is out of control and a danger to me and my children. She needs to be..."

Papa interrupted. "No more, not in her presence." He nodded toward Althea.

"Okay, but something has to be done with her."

Althea hurled obscenities at Loretta until Papa left her room and closed the door after him.

We sat down at the kitchen table. For several minutes no one spoke. Then I said, "Let's pray. We need the Lord's guidance."

Loretta said, "No, what we need is for Papa to get help from the state to deal with Althea. If not, I will find someplace else to live. I don't want my children around her any longer."

Papa got up and stood with his bent knuckles on the table. "I will do something tomorrow."

He looked directly at me. "I don't think it is a very Christian thing to do, putting your sister into an asylum."

"No, Papa, not an asylum. There is a state home for mentally disturbed children in Harrisburg. My pastor told me about it. Althea needs help that we are unable to provide."

"I know," he said, "I've looked into it myself. It's just that I hated to see this day come when we decided to abandon her."

Loretta added, "We all have suffered at her whims, especially Anna. Now it's my children, and I have to protect them."

THAT NIGHT, I KNELT BY MY BED AND PRAYED FOR MY father and Althea. I loved my sister and did not wish to see her institutionalized; however, we had no choice but to seek special care for her.

The next morning, Papa hitched up his wagon and headed for town. He never told us his intentions, but Loretta and I hoped he was not headed for the bar to drink away his responsibility for deciding what to do about Althea. I rode on the buckboard beside him because I had to work that day. We sat in silence for the first mile as Jasper made his way down the half-frozen road. I pulled my jacket collar tight against my neck and scooted close to Papa as he held the reins. He put his free arm about my shoulders.

"I love you, Anna. I hope you know that I am very proud of you."

How surprised and happy I was! "I love you too, Papa." I wish I could have added with truth, "I am proud of you too, Papa." But if I did, God would know I lied.

He fell silent again.

I asked, "Where are you going, Papa?"

He laughed heartily, his breath turning to fog in the cool morning air. "Not to the bar, honey, not this time."

"Where then?"

"Well, if you must know, I am going to see Carl Bain. He's..."

"Yes, I know who he is, Papa. He is an attorney, and he does work for the silk mill."

"I'm going to see about getting Althea some help."

"Oh, thank you, Papa." I kissed his cheek.

He seemed surprised but said nothing before getting down from the wagon. I watched as he walked across the churchyard toward the office of the law firm of Bain and Williams. I rejoiced at seeing his hand being held over the spot on his cheek where I kissed him.

WE TOLD ALTHEA SHE WAS GOING ON A VACATION and would get to ride in Brother Ralph's car. Loretta set about washing and ironing Althea's clothes. The evening before she was to leave for Harrisburg, we packed a suitcase. Papa bought a small carpet bag, which we filled with Bible stories and a book titled, *Huckleberry Finn*.

The next morning, Ralph's car arrived before seven a.m. Jerome came with him and told us he was home for good.

"The band is on the road constantly, and I miss my family too much. Ralph doesn't need me any longer, so here I am. I came home to stay."

That was good news to each of us and would have been good news to Papa, but he stayed in his room, too distraught to see Althea off. I am sure she never gave any of us a thought, even Papa, as she climbed into the seat next to Ralph.

Loretta packed a lunch of biscuits and ham for their trip. She handed the bag to Althea. She took it then threw her arms around Loretta's neck. "Goodbye," she said, "I'll see you when my vacation is over."

Loretta had tears in her eyes when she turned away from the car.

We watched without speaking until our brother and sister were out of sight. I prayed silently for God to watch over them and to make Althea well soon. Little did I know I would never see my sister again, and Papa would see her only once before he died twenty years later.

Chapter Twenty-Five

TROUBLE AT THE MILL

J ust after Christmas, we learned that a large silk mill in New York closed because of a lack of orders. It was an old mill and not very efficient. The few workers still at that mill were long-time union members with seniority. We heard rumors that these workers were claiming they had the right to displace less senior union members at our mill. When it appeared the rumors were true, our few members voted to go on strike to keep our jobs.

None of us knew what actions to take to prepare for possible violence by the New York workers. We were forced to set up picket lines around the mill. A group of New York men with guns and clubs came to the mill and threatened to break up the equipment unless they were given our jobs. We abandoned the facility. Management turned off the power to the equipment and stopped all production. The armed men refused to vacate.

One of our employees, an elderly lady, who had worked for

the mill longer than anyone else, challenged the outsiders who refused to leave.

"This town is our home, not yours. We made this mill prosper when you did not do the same in New York. We will not give up our jobs for you outsiders."

I admired her! As she defied the squatters who had overtaken our mill, she reminded me of the young women of the ILGWU who first organized to obtain fair wages and better working conditions. The New Yorkers threatened to find her husband and beat him if she did not relent to their demands. She refused. That night a group of ten or more hoodlums gathered before her lovely home and pelted the windows with rocks. Her husband, an elderly man with a serious heart problem, confronted the gang, demanding that they disband. The Sheriff arrived on scene after more than an hour of harassment by the gang and disbursed them.

My brother, Jerome, somehow got word at home that I might be in danger. He drove the horse and buggy into town. It was cold and snowing heavily, and none of us were dressed for the extreme weather we were enduring.

"Let's go inside," one of the men yelled.

But Jerome was as calm as I had ever seen him. "No, no. You will just create a larger confrontation, and someone may get injured. We need to make things uncomfortable for the men inside. Maybe they will give up and go back to New York."

He looked around and then pointed to the edge of the woods near the mill. "Let's gather wood and build a bonfire to keep warm.

"Wait them out," he said. "They will get tired of being in the dark, with no means of keeping warm."

"How long is that going to take," one of the women workers asked.

"I don't know," he said, "but if we are resolute, you will soon see them on their way back to New York."

Cheers went up. We started the fire and chatted among ourselves. After a couple of hours, quiet fell over our group as we stood around the fire. I think we had run out of hope and had nothing more to say to each other. We stood quietly for a long time, looking into the flames until they flickered, leaving only glowing half-burned logs in the pit.

Around midnight, we disbanded and met the next morning. We discussed how we might dispel the men from the mill, but decided that, since most of our workers were women, we would not be able to confront them. Jerome was willing to organize a group of husbands and brothers to get the men out of the mill, but only two of the husbands came forward.

The new plant superintendent, who had made his subtle threat against me, was desperate to bring out the completed silks and ship them off to customers. Someone would have to go into the plant while it was still occupied and remove the silks from the machines. No one volunteered, so I said I would do it, but Jerome admonished me not to endanger myself.

Brother Hiller was standing next to me. "They won't allow a man to do it, but they won't harm a woman."

"Do you want me to go?" I asked.

"I don't know anyone else who will do it, Anna. And we need to save the silk that is already on the machines."

I was scared but willing to go in if it would save our jobs, but my brother refused to let me do it alone.

"If I knew how to run the machines, I would go myself," he said. "But if Anna insists on going, I will protect her."

Jerome walked across the street to where the horse and buggy were parked. He came back carrying a shotgun. "I'm taking this with me."

By then, the sheriff arrived and wanted to know what was happening. Mr. Miller explained that the men from New York were still holed up inside and refused to leave. "I have to get the silk off the machines before I lose it. If that happens, the mill will be closed for good, I believe."

"Well," the sheriff said. "You can send someone in, but I don't want any bloodshed. So, no guns."

Jerome spoke. "If I can't take my gun, I won't go, and Anna can't go inside either."

I could have taken the opportunity to refuse to help the company, but perhaps it was my way of saying I had no hard feelings against Mr. Miller or anyone else at the mill. Besides, I had my heart set on leaving in about a month to go to Bible school. Perhaps my actions would save my job and those of all my fellow workers, even though I hoped to be leaving soon.

Mr. Miller restored power to the mill, and the sheriff escorted me through the front doors of the mill to the cheers of all the workers who were depending on me. I had no idea what kind of reception I would receive from the intruders when I turned on the machines and ran off the silk already on them. To my surprise, none of them interfered with my work as I gathered the silk from the machines. I think by then, they were cold and hungry and ready to get back home to their families.

The next day, the gang from New York abandoned the mill. The regular White Mills crews returned to work that same afternoon. But all of our actions were in vain because orders were soon cancelled by our customers, and the plant closed three weeks later. We all believed the New York union members were behind the demise of our mill.

The sting of losing my job was eased by notification a few days later of my acceptance to Practical Bible School. The Lord gives, and the Lord takes away. His will for each of us is not to be questioned even in the throes of great disappointments. He will not forsake those who believe in Him.

Chapter Twenty-Six
PREPARING TO LEAVE HOME

P rayer meetings at the homes of my church family continued while I prepared to leave home for Practical Bible College in Johnson City, New York. As I traveled along my country road, every large rock along that way became an altar. I often felt I was walking hand-in-hand with Jesus, and I would fall on my knees beside a large stone and pray and praise the Lord. During one of those prayers, a voice told me I needed to be baptized.

"Not now," I said aloud. "The rivers still have ice in them."

"Yes, now," the voice said.

I opened my eyes and looked skyward. "Surely, you don't mean now, God. I will die of pneumonia."

"Now," the voice said again.

I remembered the disciple, Peter, whom Jesus beckoned come to him, walking on the water. Peter began to sink when he lost faith and took his eyes off Christ. And here I was, alone, arguing with the angel of God who spoke to me in the wilderness along our deserted road.

It was the middle of February, and the heavy snow had just melted away. Two days later, the sun shone, and temperatures were nearly sixty degrees by mid-morning. I ran to our pastor's home. When he opened the door, I said, "I want to be baptized."

"When?"

"Now, Pastor."

"Today?"

"Yes, Pastor. That is what God wants me to do."

"Bless you, Sister, Anna. We will do it this afternoon."

Members of my church family gathered on the bank of the Wallenpaupack River in Hawley, Pennsylvania as the pastor and I waded into the freezing water, up to my waist. When the pastor lowered me into the water, a warmth I had never before experienced came over me.

"Glory be to God and my illustrious Savior, Jesus Christ," I shouted as I made my way onto the riverbank. Nothing I had ever experienced before seemed so wonderful. My fellow worshipers threw towels around me and rushed me to a waiting car. I was so filled with the glory of God that I had no thoughts of being cold or uncomfortable.

At our next prayer meeting, the pastor was suffering from a terrible cold and was unable to lead us in prayer. Brother Hiller, my former supervisor at the mill, conducted our meeting and filled in admirably. The pastor commented that whatever I had in my soul was good for all of our members.

I shouted above the chatter, "I have Jesus and that is all I need."

"Amen, amen," rolled across our little group, ending with the singing of "Amazing Grace", one of my favorite songs.

After final prayers, the pastor gave me the documents I would need to take with me to New York. My enrollment date was near the end of March. That gave me an entire month at home with nothing to do but reflect on the opportunities that awaited me in school. I had every hope that I would graduate with a better understanding of the teachings of the Bible and would learn to be more confident when ministering to my fellow Christian travelers. Each week we held services at least once, and sometimes twice, when we perceived that someone among us needed special prayers. I felt unworthy but grateful for the opportunities before me. I was thankful for my pastor's support. It gave me confidence that I could succeed at school if I believed in myself and trusted in God.

The pastor called for a special prayer meeting in his home one week before my departure, which I gratefully attended. I had no idea my fellow Christians prepared a surprise going-away party with food and small gifts. Knowing what desperate needs most of them had, made me thankful for all the small gifts I received, how I hated to leave my church family!

Despite my blessings, I worried about worldly things that confronted me. Since the mill was closed, I had no job and only five dollars. I prayed for Jesus to multiply my funds the way he did the loaves of bread and the fish for the throng of five thousand. It didn't happen just that way, but my family surprised me with help I never expected.

Ralph came home and brought with him a new pair of shoes, just my size. Loretta, who scrimped the few dollars her young husband earned playing in Ralph's band, bought me a pretty new dress. I knew how careful she was to save money; it made me so grateful for her sacrifice. The next day, Ralph and Jerome took me to Johnson City, New York, to visit the school.

The ladies in the office were kind, greeting me and giving assurances that I would be welcomed by all. The senior pastor of the school happened to stop by during my visit, and one of the ladies called his attention to me. I am certain I looked much like an orphaned waif, wearing clothing barely suitable for the New York winters. But the pastor graciously took my hand and uttered the words, "Bless you, child. Your pastor told me about you. I know you will do well here." His words reminded me of my Christian friends at home. They stayed on my mind during the return trip. How I hated to leave them! But I believed God had other callings for me.

I realized that neither of my brothers had money to spare, but when we returned home, together, they gave me four dollars. Ralph said he would have given me more, but he needed to save for gas to drive me back to Johnson City the following week. It was then I realized how the suffering we had gone through for all the years as children only made us stronger and made us love each other more than ever. At least, we owed that much to our mother and father.

My experiences growing up left me with insecurities, which I have done my best to overcome. I wondered how I would fit in with the young people at Bible school. I assumed they had lived normal lives with caring mothers and fathers they could be proud of. And I assumed their parental guidance led them to Practical Bible College. But, as you know by now, I had no such parental guidance. I found God in the wilderness. I traveled each day to and from work. I was tutored by believing Christians and loving friends. I was forced to grow up before my time and had never had young friends, and I wondered how I would interact with them and how I would adjust to their young ways. I was determined they would never learn of the dysfunction I experienced during my nineteen years of life before Practical Bible College.

I was not the only child in the family to suffer mistreatment. My siblings experienced it also, each of us with our own particular burdens to bear. We disclosed some things to each other; mostly, we bore them alone. But with each indignity and each cruelty by our parents, we became stronger and learned to overcome whatever obstacles may burden our paths.

I have done my utmost to follow God's command that I honor my father and mother. However, there are so many awful events in my life at home that will forevermore remain unspoken. I have not mentioned them in this memoir because revealing them will serve no purpose, and they would do nothing to glorify God. They are buried with the past, and there they will remain.

Chapter Twenty-Seven

ON TO BIBLE SCHOOL

What would life be like if troubles never came our way? I suppose we may even begin to believe we have no need for God's intervention in our lives. Once again, my faith in Him was reinforced when, the day before I was to leave for Bible school, Ralph sent word that his car had suffered a broken axle and he would be unable to drive me to New York. For a moment, I was overcome with panic. Then I remembered Jesus saying, "I will never forsake thee." I knelt and prayed. A voice told me to go to my pastor's house.

The weather was still severe in March. I put on my heaviest coat and set out on the three-mile walk. The pastor was not surprised to see me when I arrived an hour later.

"You have been on my mind this morning, Anna. I was concerned about your travel arrangements. I know you told me your brothers were taking you, but God made me wary that something might go wrong."

The pastor and his wife had been so kind to me. I hated to impose by asking him to drive me to New York, but I had no choice. I'm sure tears were in my eyes, and I was almost choking when I blurted out the words, "Ralph's car is broken, and he can't take me tomorrow."

The pastor smiled and took my hand. "I felt in my soul that something was wrong this morning. But don't worry. You can ride with my wife and me. We will be there to assist with registration and to celebrate your new beginning in life. My wife will help you get settled into your room."

We prayed together then the pastor drove me home. When his car was out of sight, my mind was finally at ease remembering how desperate I felt that morning when I learned of Ralph's car problems. I will always believe Jesus intervened with my pastor and made him aware of my troubles before I arrived at his home that day.

Next morning at seven, I was ready to leave. My heart was jumping with joy. Over and over, I thanked God for the opportunities waiting for me at the school. When I saw the pastor's car in the distance, I called to Papa, Jerome, and Loretta. They stood with me as I waited impatiently, the three or four minutes for the car to arrive at our front porch.

The pastor placed my only suitcase into the back seat along with a small duffle bag, holding the few toiletries I possessed. He shook hands with Papa and Jerome, then kissed Loretta's cheek.

"Bless all of you," he said. "And don't worry about your Anna. She will be in God's hands."

I have never understood why I cried when our car pulled away and drove down our frozen dirt road. I was so happy and excited about the opportunities lying ahead, and yet, I was crying. Perhaps, it was the acts of kindness my brothers and sister showed me during my last few days at home. It made me realize how much we loved each other. And it was unfair that I was escaping a hell they appeared destined to perish in. I would always be grateful, and they would be part of every prayer I uttered.

I had no idea what the word, "registration", meant. It was the first thing we did upon arrival at the school. After settling in our rooms, the new students were treated to a sumptuous banquet. I had never seen so much food, so many choices, fish, chicken, potatoes, and vegetables of all kinds. A piece of chocolate cake with ice cream was served at the end. With each bite, I was reminded of all the times my siblings and I had gone to bed hungry. How I wished they could share some of the food on my plate!

During our meal, each pastor stood and introduced his student. My pastor said so many nice things about me it made me think he was speaking about someone else. I admit that it was good to be compared to saints, but I was certain I could never measure up to the accolades he praised me with. I was not only amazed by his words; I was also embarrassed, realizing what a high bar he had set for me with his introduction. When he finished speaking, he asked if I had anything I wished to say.

It troubled me to think I might not be able to live up to all the wonderful things my pastor said. I had to think for a moment about how I should respond. When I collected my thoughts, I spoke.

"Yes," I said in a voice that must have been difficult for people at the end of my table to hear, "I thank Jesus, for it is only by His grace that I am among so many loving Christians.

And I thank you and your wife, pastor, and all my church friends at home for their support and good wishes."

The staff members and other students clapped their hands, and I heard some of them uttering the word "Amen." For I am sure they felt as I did: *Only by God's grace am I here.*

I am sure you can imagine how out of place I felt at the banquet table. There were extra forks and spoons and napkins, so many that I didn't know which to use first. I watched my pastor and others at the table to make sure I never used the wrong utensil. I studied Amy Vanderbilt's books on manners before leaving home and remembered, having read, that if a person sat close to you on the right, you should eat with your left hand. Since I was unhandy using my left hand, I dabbled desperately at my food and ended up eating little. However, the dessert was much too good to waste. I ate all of it with my right hand, and I was careful to keep my elbows off the table.

After dinner, the pastor and his wife accompanied me to my room. There, they gave me a surprise gift box containing a Bible, notebook paper, pencils, and an ink pen with a bottle of blue ink.

"You have no excuse for not writing to us, Anna," the pastor's wife said, "and we will answer every letter. All your friends at home will be anxious to hear from you. And so will the pastor and I."

"I promise to write at least once a month," I told her.

Even though I was filled with excitement at the thought of starting school, I feared I would feel intimidated when I was alone. Thoughts of the night I spent in the empty apartment building after my abduction came to mind. Even though I was much older, the fear of being on my own was real as when I was six years old. *But I have Jesus now, and that is sufficient,* I told myself.

As my pastor and his wife bid me goodbye and drove away, I felt very empty. But soon, I met my roommate, and by the next day, I was caught up in the activities, the work schedule, and preparations for attending my first class. I was eager to learn how to be a better Christian and to become a graduate of Practical Bible College.

Chapter Twenty-Eight

GOOD GRADES AND GEORGE

My roommate was a girl by the name of Ruth Munson. As we became acquainted, I learned that her problems at home, though unlike mine, left her with a severe inferiority complex. She was a complainer, unable to deal with the simplest setbacks without playing the part of a victim. I could have told her about my own familial problems, in many ways, more devastating than hers, but I chose not to do it. I had sympathy for her but could not understand why she would not put the past behind her and be grateful for her opportunities at Practical Bible College.

She came from a family of six children. Her mother passed away when she was only sixteen. As the eldest child, she was unable to handle the burdens of caring for her younger sisters and keeping house for her father. I thought about the parallels between her life and my sister, Margie. Such thoughts made me realize how much a strong belief in Almighty God is essential to overcoming one's difficulties. Margie believed in Him to the end, even when she was subjected to Anthony's cruelty. I soon realized that Ruth did not take her troubles to Jesus Christ in prayer as Margie did but complained about them to anyone who would listen. Since I was her roommate, I heard much about her problems, and I heard them often.

Ruth got into Bible school because of her pastor's recommendation. He and her father thought it would give her mental stability. God will do that, but He requires us to hunger and pray for His intervention in our lives.

"My father was afraid I was cracking up, so they sent me here."

And not to serve God? I thought.

I dared not say I believed such a reason was hypocritical and displeasing to God, but I was not Ruth's judge; I was her roommate and would do all I could to be a good friend and help keep her on a righteous path. Often that was difficult, sometimes affecting my own optimism. She was eighteen, a year younger than me, but she relied on me as if I were an older sister.

Sometimes when I was frustrated, I would admonish her for being so negative about everything and everybody. As my papa might say, she had a lazy streak a mile wide and lay on her bed while I struggled with my homework and studies.

"Why are you here, Ruth?"

"Because my dad wanted me to come."

"You are not here to learn about God and how to live for him?"

"Yes, that too, Anna, but more than anything, I needed to get away from a desperate situation. I admire you for your strong beliefs and ability to cope with adversity. I just don't have that willpower in me."

"Neither do I," I said. "I leave it to Jesus. He sees me through all my struggles. The Lord will not forsake us if we call on him. You need to memorize the Twenty-Third Psalm:

The Lord is my shepherd; I shall not want.

"I wish I had your faith, Anna, but it is a struggle for me after all I have been through."

"That is why you are here, Sister Ruth, to learn how to hear Jesus when he has something to say to you. That is why both of us are here."

My pep talks had little effect, and she continued her habit of complaining about everything that did not suit her. I hummed hymns as I studied, trying to drown out her whining. Instead of doing her homework in the evening, she napped in between gripes, after which she would copy my papers and turn them in as her own.

I grew impatient with her and thought of asking to be paired with another roommate, but I did not wish to cause more problems for Ruth. So, I endured the situation for the first semester and hid my homework after it was finished. Ruth did not return for the second semester. I often wondered what happened in her life, and I have uttered many prayers on her behalf.

DESPITE THE PROBLEMS I EXPERIENCED WITH RUTH, school was an exhilarating process for me. Just knowing that I was becoming a better Christian lifted me above the daily struggles.

Our meals were not sumptuous compared to the banquet meal, but we had nourishing food and plenty of it. At the evening meal, I often sang hymns that the teachers or my fellow students requested. A girl by the name of Sylvia often accompanied me on the autoharp. I was happy to sing for my friends and to please God.

All our teachers were conscientious, Bible-taught men of God. One of them had quaint expressions that sometimes confounded other students and me. I soon learned to ignore them and accept the good lessons he taught all of us.

I don't want you to get the idea that school was easy. It was not. I had to study hard, but it paid off. My grades averaged one hundred in every subject, earning me the respect and praise of my teachers. They made me realize, for the first time in my life, that I was not inferior to other people, but in fact, I carried the highest grades in my class. That was such a great feeling, especially after the shame that Althea and I experienced as young children in our school at home.

By December, I had been away from home for eight months. School was closed for a month during the holidays. All my classmates were busy preparing to go home until school began again in January. I couldn't remain at school, and I wondered how I would get home. As always, when I faced a dilemma, I turned to God, asking him to give me one more miracle.

The next day, my new friend, Wilma Wharton, asked me what I was doing for the holidays.

"Nothing," I said. "I will try to get in touch with my brother or pastor for a ride home."

"Why don't you come home with me? My father will be picking me up on Saturday."

"I would love to," I said, never letting Wilma know how relieved I was and how much I appreciated her invitation. I thanked God that night because I knew he sent Wilma to me.

What a quiet, delightful, homespun atmosphere! Her father and mother were faithful Christians. He was kind and given to telling tall tales we all enjoyed hearing. Most of them had a moral based on a biblical verse. Her mother had just come home from the hospital after a bout with pneumonia. But she refused to allow anyone to wait on her. She was a wonderful cook and sang as she prepared our meals. She seemed surprised and happy when I joined her singing. She made me feel as if I was her daughter.

This is what family really means, I thought, for the first time in my life, feeling as though I had been deprived of my childhood by parents who failed to honor God. Even though we were a poor family, our lives could have been so much better if we had all just loved and supported each other. Wilma's family was a perfect example of what God could do for us if we only believe in Him.

The day I arrived, Wilma's brother came home from Scranton, where he was working on a job for the city. A friend of his by the name of George Gamble came home with him. After dinner, we sat around the table as a family, enjoying fellowship and exchanging funny stories. Then I was asked to sing, accompanying myself by chording on their piano. Wilma's father requested "The Beautiful Garden of Prayer," his favorite song.

"It has never sounded better," he said.

My face burned with embarrassment because George was watching me. I knew I would see that same look on his face many more times.

Chapter Twenty-Nine

GEORGE AND ME

After dinner and our wonderful fellowship and singing, we went bobsledding. Snow was falling along with the temperatures. We girls wore men's overalls, and I am sure we looked like vagabonds. George and Wilma's brother, Bill sat up front; Bill drove the bobsled while Wilma and I sat behind them. What great fun we had!

We stopped on a sloping hillside, got off, and pelted each other with snowballs. After a while, we fell breathlessly into the snow. George drove toward home after we were back on the bobsled. As we sang "Jingle Bells," he had no idea I had both hands filled with snow. Just as he opened his mouth widest, singing to the top of his voice, I reached over the seat and washed his face. He let out a yell and then stopped the horse. He jumped off and grabbed a handful of snow. I guess you would say he gave me a dose of my own medicine because he got even by washing my face with a handful of wet snow.

. . .

I̲t̲ ̲m̲u̲s̲t̲ ̲h̲a̲v̲e̲ ̲b̲e̲e̲n̲ ̲e̲v̲i̲d̲e̲n̲t̲ ̲t̲o̲ ̲e̲v̲e̲r̲y̲o̲n̲e̲ ̲t̲h̲a̲t̲ I liked George very much, and I suppose, just as obvious that he liked me. He was leaving the next day to get his brother, Raymond, for Christmas. I think Mr. Wharton saw how well George and I got along and wanted to play Cupid.

"George, aren't you going to Hawley tomorrow to get your brother?"

"Yes, if my old car will make it."

"The Lord will see you there," Mr. Wharton said. "And maybe you could give Anna a ride home since White Mills is only two or three miles out of your way."

George's smile told me he liked the idea as much as I did.

"That would be great," he said. "But I need to clean my car before Anna can get in. There is so much junk in it. We guys aren't as neat as the girls."

What a ride that was. He drove a Ford coupe with side curtains, and it was freezing cold. I piled all my belongings between us, so I wouldn't have to sit so close to him. We were almost frozen when we arrived at my dad's home. George made himself at home, took off his shoes, and put his feet on the side of the heating stove.

I think George endeared himself to my father and Jerome right away. He sat with his feet propped on the side of our stove for at least an hour. Then he put on his shoes and stood.

"I better get going. My brother is expecting me."

"Come back any time," My father said. "You seem like a nice young man."

That was such an unlikely comment by Papa. He never liked most people, especially any boy who ever showed an interest in me.

"I'll come back and get her before her school starts."

Thinking about the miserable cold on our trip home made me have second thoughts about riding back with George, but I was thankful for his generosity, and I knew I wanted to spend time again with him. On the return trip, I would not put my belongings between us.

As we drove back to school, we were at ease with each other, and we joked and laughed all the way. When I unpacked at school, I found that George had hidden candy in my luggage. I couldn't get him off my mind for the next several days, but I was determined not to get too interested in him because he would be a distraction from my studies.

George and I had so much in common, and I knew I was very attracted to him. My mother was never really present in my life, and George's mother wasn't present in his life either. She died of tuberculosis when he was only six. His family lived in poverty, and like me, he felt that he did not measure up to others.

George's father remarried shortly after his mother passed away. His stepmother gave birth to nine children. George was the eldest child in the mixed family and received most of the harsh treatment meted out by his stepmother. Even now, I wonder how he became such a kind and gentle man with a great sense of humor. It must have been his deep faith in God, which he always exhibited in his caring demeanor.

I had never known what it was like to be in love, but I thought it was happening to me. When I prayed before class, I would see George's face. I prayed for Jesus to let me know I was not being sinful by thinking of George when I prayed. *It is good,* a voice said. *He is a God-fearing young man.*

Following a week of praying in that manner, some students and I were asked to take part in a choir directed by John Young in a big theatre in Binghamton. The evangelist was John Rice, editor of "The Sword of the Lord" paper. As we students dismounted from the choir loft, it seemed natural that George should be standing there waiting for me. He was talking with two Nazarene ladies as I approached him. He appeared eager to tell me, in their presence, that he had surrendered his life to God and given up dances—one worldly pleasure he enjoyed. I told him it was good to dance as long as he never lost sight of Jesus Christ. We saw each other every weekend after that.

The school assigned me a new roommate, a sixty-five-year-old lady who was returning to school for a refresher course. At night, she tucked me into bed and said a short prayer for both of us.

Now I lay me down to sleep,
I pray the Lord my soul to keep.
If I should die before I wake,
I pray the Lord my soul to take.

"We are never too old to learn more about Jesus," she told me. "I hunger for knowledge about his life and the good he did for the sick and lame. I yearn to feel his dread as he was taken away to be hung on the cross. I want to share his forgiveness of those who persecuted him. I want to feel the glory of the criminal who hung on a cross beside Jesus. How relieved he must have felt when Jesus told the man he would be with Him in Heaven that day. That is why I am here with you, to learn more about my Savior."

How I yearned for the ability to express my love for Jesus the way she did. I vowed then never to stop trying to know more about Him. "Maybe I will come back to school when I'm older. I know I'll still want to learn," I said.

I think she believed it was her duty to protect me from evil. She was so cute when she gave me motherly advice about boys. She was horrified when I told her I was falling in love with George and that I had dated him without the school's permission.

"Never let a boy put his arm around you until you are married. Once, Mr. Biggs put his arm along the back of the seat behind me, and I made him stay away for six months."

I laughed. "It's a wonder he ever married you."

"He respected me then, and he would still today if he was alive."

"Please don't tell the school I dated George. We only went for walks and talked with each other. I've never kissed him, but I'm sure it would be nice."

At the end of that school year, I decided I didn't have the capacity or education to continue with additional studies. I had skipped all my high school subjects—including English—which was essential for studies in Greek and deeper biblical courses.

George and I were married the following October at the Baptist parsonage in Maine, New York. We had only fifty dollars between us. We paid seven dollars for the first month's rent on a large ten-room house in the country near his home.

George got three days off from Endicott Johnson, where he was employed. We took a trip to Thousand Islands in a borrowed car, much nicer than the one that George drove me home in that Christmas when we first met.

After our return, the minister of the Glen Aubrey church asked us to attend his church to help the new minister who was taking over as pastor. We agreed and attended regularly and participated in many church activities. He was a particularly good man and asked me to take charge of the Boosters, a young people's Christian group. That allowed me to use what I had learned at Practical Baptist College.

We made great friends among our new church family, and I enjoyed fellowshipping with those who were only a few years younger than I was. Things were not always easy, but thank God, George and I were together, and Jesus Christ was still the Lord of our lives.

Chapter Thirty
BEING MOM

Two months after we moved into the farmhouse, I learned I was pregnant. My first child, Mary Lou, was born eight months later. It was a difficult pregnancy because I suffered from acute toxemia that landed me in the hospital for a month. My doctor ordered me to lie on my back, which I did for two weeks without moving. My blood pressure was excessive even though I had been on a strict diet for weeks.

My hospital room was adjacent to the delivery room, allowing me to hear all the young mothers' screams during labor and delivery. I became very frightened. I could vividly remember the terrible agony my sister, Margie, experienced when she was trying to deliver her son, who was born dead. And ultimately, the gruesome end to her life following thirteen convulsions and an entire night of suffering. That thought made me wonder if my baby and I would survive. I was not afraid of death because I knew I would be safe in the arms of

Jesus, but I wanted my baby to live even if I did not. Finally, the day arrived, and our beautiful baby was born, but I was too ill to see her for several hours. My blood pressure had risen to dangerous levels during childbirth. Six hours later, the nurse brought her to me.

Since I gave my life to Jesus, so many things have happened that I cannot explain. While lying in the hospital, unable to move or hear anyone speak, I constantly heard a beautiful chorus singing. I could hear the music but never understood the words. When the lady who shared a room with me spoke, I could see her lips moving but could not hear her. The chorus in my head sang louder when she appeared to be speaking. The music continued for three days. No one else ever heard a note, and I have never understood where the music came from. Maybe God will explain it all to me someday when I am in Heaven with Jesus.

After a week, we brought our beautiful baby home, and both George and I were happy the ordeal was over. I will always be grateful that he knew how to care for infants. I was too emaciated and weak to care for her alone, and George carried much of the burden for the first two months.

Mary Lou suffered from cholic and required constant attention. Nothing we gave her seemed to help. When George was not at work, the baby was usually on his shoulder as he tried to pacify her. When she cried, I cried along with her. After four or five months, Mary Lou became a delightful and happy baby, and I thanked God for seeing me through a period when my faith faltered. In retrospect, I concluded I did not pray enough or turn my troubles over to my Savior.

When I was first married, I asked God for four children, two boys and two girls, and I added, "Please, God, let them be singers." But after giving birth to Mary Lou and living through four months of her crying, I had second thoughts. George consoled me, and we prayed together that my next pregnancy would be much easier. God gave us a healthy baby boy two years later. We named him Jerome, after my oldest brother.

After more than a year of trying, we began to believe we would have no more children. However, James was born two years later, and our prayers were answered again when Marie was born eighteen months after the birth of James. Each of my children was so different from the others, and I have always appreciated their differences. Thankfully, they were all good singers, and the surviving ones still are, especially my daughter, Marie. We love to sing duets whenever we are able to spend time together.

Raising four children just when the nation was coming out of a depression was difficult. It was made even more so when the war ended, and jobs were scarce because veterans returned home and regained their jobs. We moved wherever George could find work. When our children were young, we lived in one-room schoolhouses, carried water from a well, and used an outside toilet. We had no electricity. I scrubbed our clothes on a washboard and ironed them with a flatiron heated on the woodstove top. George's work was never easy, but he always found time to help me with the children in the evening.

After James was born, we moved to a farm in south Owego, New York. Marie soon arrived, making our family complete. The children loved the farm, and we were all happy there. The only problem was that the children did not see much of their father except on weekends. He worked nights, and I was left alone. He slept a part of each day but made sure he had a little time in the evening for his family.

One night when I was alone with our children, our dog began barking at the door. When he wouldn't stop, I turned him outside. I could hear the commotion but was afraid to go out to check on the dog. George had slaughtered a pig that day, and I remembered it was hanging on the side of the shed. He planned to butcher the pig the next day and salt it for storage in our shed to provide meat for our family for at least six months.

At daybreak, I went outside and found the pig in the snow. Our dog had chased away someone who attempted to steal our meat during the night. We thought about who might have tried to rob us, but our closest neighbors were nearly a mile away. All of them attended church with us, and no one but our family knew George was slaughtering a pig. He decided some stranger must have wandered onto our property and saw an opportunity to take our pig. Afterward, I was very wary of being left alone while George worked, but there was little I could do except trust in God to keep us safe.

Our children attended school in Owego and caught a bus that ran about a mile from our house. One day, Mary brought home a note saying they were not allowed to ride on the school bus to Owego anymore because we were just over the district line. The alternative would be for the children to walk three miles to a different small school that was closed for at least one month during the winter each year. It was bad enough that our youngest son, James, cried because he had to walk to and from the bus. We couldn't make him walk six miles each day, so we took him out of school for a year.

We obtained books for James and assigned him schoolwork at home. He was constantly ill and spent much of his day sleeping. His complaining sent me into despair. He cried so much I thought he was trying to get attention. We took him to a specialist who recommended removing his tonsils and adenoids. When he was a teenager, we learned the tonsillectomy was unnecessary. James suffered from polio when he was very young, and one leg was shorter than the other.

We faced his problems with optimism and prayers. A year later, the doctors said he was cured. He always walked with a slight limp but showed no other effects of polio. We thanked God for that blessing among so many others that He sent our way.

I had four children for which I prayed. God answered so many of my prayers that I felt guilt when I longed for something more. Fortunately, we had a decent place to live and raise our children. But it was very lonely in the country with George away so often at work.

I remember kneeling outdoors in the evenings after putting the children to bed. I said aloud, "Oh, God, please find us a place in town." Then I would think to myself, *that's asking for a miracle.* To remain on the farm, we needed at least one hundred dollars to pay off the loan, and we would need another hundred dollars to pay for a new furnace. The only things we owned outright were our two horses. We ended up selling them and got enough to repair the furnace.

I asked George, "What will we do for a horse next spring?"

"God will provide," he said. "And we will do what he tells us."

I could always depend on George to lift my spirits when I had doubts. It was God's will that we were together, and I thank Him for the bobsled ride so many years ago.

Chapter Thirty-One

NEAR TRAGEDY TO TRIUMPH

W e never know when God will bless us. He does things in his own time and when we least expect it. Often, we do not recognize His good works even when they are occurring. That was exemplified for us two weeks after we sold our horses when He showed His loving care.

Dr. Adolph Mahler and his son Bill were holding revival meetings and requested that I sing. Before George left for work, he had cautioned me that a severe storm was coming. I was practicing singing on the porch that afternoon when I saw the clouds rolling overhead. I was not watching the children closely. They were starting for the barn to play in the hay when Mary changed her mind. I heard her say, "Dad doesn't want us playing in the hay." She called her brothers and sister back to the house, and they all came inside.

Moments after the children were in the house, I heard a violent explosion. I ran to the edge of the porch and looked out. The barn had been struck by lightning and was going up in flames. How fortunate it was that our horses had been sold and were not inside the barn. Our milk cow was in the field and not in any danger either. I fell to my knees and thanked God for turning my children around before the bolt of lightning occurred.

I dreaded telling George about the barn when he came home, but he saw the remains of it as soon as he drove into our yard. I ran out to meet him.

Pointing toward what was left of the barn, I said. "It was lightning." I was nearly in tears.

George told me not to worry. "It's insured."

The insurance money paid off the farm, and we began saving money to buy another horse for plowing in the spring.

I was resigned that we would not move from the farm, which we now owned entirely. The children were getting bigger and were more company and comfort to me. I was able to cope better with George being away at work much of the time.

They say that lightning does not strike twice in the same place. I am living proof that it isn't so. Once more, lightning struck, and this time it hit the house. I was only seconds away from being electrocuted. Thankfully, my God stepped in and saved me because He still had good works that He wanted me to do.

A storm was raging outside while I washed dishes in a pan warming on the stove. When I saw flashes of lightning in the distance, I thought of our two beagle pups that were chained to a metal pipe outside. I ran out into the rain and put the dogs in their pen where they could get shelter. I came back to the stove to finish washing the dishes, but before I put my hands in the water, a terrifying explosion occurred in the stove. It crossed the sink leaving a hole in the side of the refrigerator.

The insurance investigator said he felt like he was looking at a ghost, that I should not have survived, and neither should the house. We received just enough money to buy a used refrigerator and a new stove. Although I was thankful for being spared and having a decent home for my children, I did not wish to chance another lightning strike. George and I began to think seriously about moving into town. We could sell our farm, but that would take a long time, and we had no money for a down payment. But God gave me the answer.

I called a real estate man and arranged to sell trees from our farm. The sale raised just enough to make needed repairs to the house with a small amount left over. I had no new ideas for raising the rest of the money we needed for the down payment, but I believed God would supply our needs.

At Easter time, an unexpected visitor arrived for a short stay. My brother, Jerome, came to our house in Owego for the first time. Years had gone by since we last saw each other, so we had a lot to talk about. As improbable as it may seem, we found humor in the terrible experiences we had as children. I told him of my narrow escapes from lightning and that we were saving for a house in town. I had no idea about Jerome's financial situation, but I learned he was a successful business owner.

"Let me know when you find the place you want, and I'll lend you the money for a down payment."

"We couldn't." I protested.

"Yes," Jerome said. "If anyone deserves it, you do."

Praise God! I have talked about Him working in mysterious ways. As I have written in this memoir, He has done wonderous things for me over and over. Even when I faltered in my faith, He rescued me. If I live to be one hundred, I can never do enough good works to repay my Savior.

Don't tell me of coincidences. God has a hand in everything. He is always there for us if we want Him. Two days after Jerome's visit a lady from the Christian and Missionary Alliance (C&MA) Church called to tell us about a home for sale near Owego. Jerome bought the contract, and we moved in the next month. We faithfully paid off our debt to him with money from the sale of the farm and the few savings bonds we bought during the war. The C&MA Church became home to George and me, and I am still a member. George was an elder until his death ten years ago.

Our children spent their young lives growing up in that house on the outskirts of Owego, a small village that seemed a perfect place to live as a child. Our whole family sang and harmonized just as I had prayed. We practiced songs on our front porch. I played baseball with George and the children. They had freedom to roam almost anywhere, and so they did. My children's lives were not always easy as they became teenagers and then adults. George and I did our utmost to instill in them the gifts of faith, love, and music. All my children love Jesus and want to please Him by living faithful lives.

For many years, I was in charge of the children's church programs. On Sunday mornings before church, our family visited a prison where we sang songs glorifying God. I sang solos and duets with Marie, who loved singing as much as I did.

George and I did our best to honor God by caring for the needy. We adopted his oldest nephew, John, when he was twelve and raised him as our own. We heard of a Vietnamese couple with three children and a niece that needed help after the end of the war, and we took them in for more than a year. They still call me Mom.

I stayed busy with God's work for as long as possible. When church members were sick or did not attend services, I wrote cards with comforting words and assurances that God loved them. Because people are not perfect, problems sometimes arose in our church. George and I did not take sides in any disputes, and we never lost sight of our first love, God.

Chapter Thirty-Two

BACK TO WHITE MILLS

I never planned to return to White Mills even though I had many fond memories of my church family and some of the workers I saw every day at the silk mill. I would have loved visiting with Brother Hiller and the dear pastor who baptized me, but they had gone to meet Jesus in Heaven, both passing at young ages.

As for my family, it was still in disarray. My brother, Ralph, and his band went on the road, living most of the time in a small city called Bristol, Virginia, where country music was being broadcast over the radio. Loretta's husband was still part of Ralph's band, and he left her at home, where she cared for Papa and her two children. Jerome never married. His business ventures kept him on the road most of the time. I understand our mother visited only once, months after I left for Practical Bible College, and she had not been back since then. Loretta and I used to write to each other often. She said our mother corresponded with Althea and sent religious books to her at

Christmas and other special days (God does work in wonderous ways).

I learned from Jerome, during his visit, that Papa, at seventy, was almost incapacitated and suffering from the long-term effects of arsenic poisoning. His toes turned under so much that he could no longer wear shoes or play his beloved accordion because of his twisted fingers. Fortunately, Jerome was well off and could take care of the family's financial needs.

Long ago, I forgave my father and mother for my mistreatment and the disunity and dysfunction we suffered as children. It permanently affected all of us. I was fortunate that God showed me how to overcome what I endured as a child.

George and I were busy settling into our new home near Owego, and we had little time to think about the travails of others. But that changed with a telegram from Jerome, who was in New Orleans, Louisiana. He informed us that Papa had passed, and Loretta was incapable of making funeral arrangements. He sent us a phone number where he could be reached.

"My car is at the airport in Washington, D.C. I will arrive there tomorrow afternoon and then drive home."

"What can George and I do right now?" I asked.

"I need you to go home and take charge of things until I get there the day after tomorrow."

Mary, my eldest child, was eleven and mature for her age, but I did not dare leave her home to care for our other children. I called one of our church members, and she agreed to stay with the children for four or five days. George and I packed our car and set out for White Mills that afternoon, arriving about six p.m. Loretta was an emotional wreck but had the good sense to call the coroner, who came to the house and examined Papa's body. By the time we arrived, his body had been taken to the funeral home in White Mills.

My greatest concern was for Papa's soul. I wondered if he repented or professed a renewal of his belief in Jesus Christ, which had surfaced at times in the past, even when he was in one of his most cruel moods. The thought occurred to me that he might have been drunk when he went to meet his Maker. I prayed not.

"No," Loretta said. "He gave up drinking at least six months before he became incapacitated."

"Have you heard from Mother? Someone needs to let her know Papa's gone."

"No. I thought Althea might know how to get in touch with her, so I called. She was going through one of her episodes and was incoherent. She didn't appear to know who I was, or Mother and Papa, for that matter."

"Did Mother ever write to you or Jerome? Maybe you can find one of her letters with a return address," I said.

Loretta shook her head. "I thought of that too. I've torn the house apart, looking for a letter with her address on it. I don't think it matters because Mother moved so often. Even if we could find an address, it would not be where she lives now. There is no hope with Althea. I think she has forgotten all of us."

It was too late to go to the funeral home. George called to let the director know we would be in to see him the next morning. The thought occurred to me that I had not shed a single tear for my father. How sad that he left this world after seventy years and ten children, none of whom would truly

mourn his passing. I attempted to think of the good things
Papa did. He imbued in all his children a love of music and, at
times, showed a tender side that belied his bitterness. I recalled
the summer we worked together in the field, planting and
harvesting crops. If all my childhood could have been like that
summer, I would have adored my father.

Tears began to flow down my cheeks, not so much because
Papa was gone. I was crying for the mother I never had and
what might have been—all the parental love my siblings and I
had never experienced as children. God says to honor thy father
and thy mother. Returning to White Mills for my father's
funeral was as close as I could come to comply with God's
commandment. After Papa's funeral, I would close that
unhappy chapter of my life.

"Did Papa say anything before he passed?"

"Not at the end," Loretta said. "But a few days before he
went, he opened his eyes and spoke mother's name, *Della,
Della.*"

"How sad," I said.

"One other thing. He asked for Horton over and over and
then went silent. He never spoke after that."

"Poor Horton, Papa loved that little boy more than
anything else in the world, more than any other one of us, and
Horton never even recognized Papa."

Chapter Thirty-Three
PREPARING TO MEET JESUS

M any years have elapsed since I wrote in this book, eight years, to be exact. My recollections were interrupted by a heart attack about the time I was writing of George and me. To be honest, he always had that effect on me, stopping my heart when I saw him or thought about him. We loved each other dearly, and I remain devoted to his memory today. Of course, the first love in my life is Jesus Christ, my Lord and Savior, and George shared that love for Him with me.

My faith in God did not waiver with the health issues I endured at age seventy, and He cured me without lasting residual effects. After being diagnosed with heart failure, I had an inner ear problem that left me unable to stand alone for two months. In 1993, at age seventy-five, I experienced dizziness that incapacitated me for several weeks. The doctors finally decided I had a cranial fault. That diagnosis made me laugh as I told myself, "I always knew I had a hole in my head."

As I said earlier, George died at age seventy-two. He had

the kindest heart of any man I ever knew. His last thoughts were for me, calling me to his bedside minutes before he passed, telling me not to live alone after he was gone. My sight was failing badly, and I had been declared legally blind. George was afraid I would not be able to get along by myself. After his death, I moved into a senior housing apartment, where I lived until 2010. I was aided by church members who still called me "Mom." When I was ninety-two, my daughter, Marie, convinced me to move into the convalescent center in Ypsilanti, Michigan, where I would be close enough for her to visit occasionally. Now that I am settled in my new surroundings, I have decided to add these last few words to my memoir before I am taken home to be with Jesus.

For the benefit of my two living children, my grandchildren, and my great-grandchildren, I will sum up this memoir by reasserting my faith in God and thanking Him for sending His son to die on the cross for my sins. At this time, my health is good, considering my age and the ailments I have endured. I feel wonderful; I do not experience any discomfort, so I praise God for my good health, energy, and sanity. Most of all, I praise my great physician, who heals all my diseases. I realize I'm getting older, so I can't expect my good fortunes to last forever, but I praise Him for all He has done and for whatever may come next. I also praise God for George, the wonderful man I married seventy-two years ago.

Children, when you read this in years to come, remember that my love extends to each of you today. I expect none of you to mourn for me because I will be at peace, looking down on you from Heaven's door.

Praise Be to God Almighty.

Third Interlude

I finished reading Anna's account of her life at two a.m. in the morning. My mind was roiling with a mixture of emotions, admiration, empathy, sadness, joy, and a questioning of my own agnosticism. We read in the Bible of prophets chosen by God to promulgate His message of love, salvation, and damnation. I pondered the lives of those chosen prophets, and wondered if any believed His Word more than Anna Marie Gamble and was more deserving of His love and protection. No one I ever knew was more obedient to His Word than she or more determined to live a life pleasing to Him.

For three evenings, I had been engrossed in her story, wondering how it would end, only to find that her life held struggles from her childhood until the day we met at the convalescent center in Ypsilanti. Through it all, her faith never failed her. I thought of the lessons anyone who may read this account would take away from her experiences. Someone needed to tell her story. I decided I would attempt to do it. It continues in the chapters that follow. I trust that I have done Anna Marie Gamble justice.

Chapter Thirty-Four

UNDERSTANDING ANNA

It was drizzling and unusually cold for late September when I arrived at the convalescent center the next morning. By then, Mary had been at the facility for three months, and Anna was in her seventh year of residency. I always arrived promptly at nine-thirty a.m. By then, the patients would have finished their morning meals, and Anna would be prowling the hallways, restless and inquisitive. Most mornings, she was the first patient I encountered in the corridor, but not that morning. It always concerned me if I did not hear her singing or playing her harmonica when I passed her room. Since I heard nothing, I knocked, then pushed open the door. Anna looked up from her bedside chair and smiled.

"What are you doing, Anna?"

"Praying," she said as she rose from her chair. "Do you need me to pray for you?"

"Someone should," I said.

"Young man." She shook her finger in my direction. "Don't make light of your eternal salvation."

"No, no, Anna, I mean someone should pray for me. I would appreciate it if you included me in your prayers."

"Then I will do it." She closed her door, leaving me standing with what I assumed was a puzzled look on my face.

With the soothing sounds of "Amazing Grace" following me, I walked down the hall to Mary's room. It was good to know that Anna was doing what she enjoyed most, singing and making music. I wondered where her mind went when she played masterfully on her harmonica because she appeared to be in a world of her own. My heart ached for the shadow that must have once been a remarkably accomplished woman, and I marveled at the equanimity with which she faced the uncertainty that lay just beyond each fragile moment of lucidity. I was awed by the courage with which she clung to bits and pieces of a once purposeful life. As I stood by Mary's door until Anna finished playing, I imagined she would then make her daily sojourn to the aquarium, where she seemed to be most at peace.

She was capable of rational discourse in her lucid moments, but she could abruptly depart from reality and begin talking nonsensically. Usually, she addressed me as "Young Man", so I was surprised when one morning she called me "Papa" and, afterward, did so frequently. I wondered if she was thinking of her father in a good light or as an oppressor. I never knew which but stopped worrying about it when she began calling me "Pastor." Happily, "Young Man" seemed to be her favorite appellation for me, and it was definitely mine.

And so, our days went by. My life not only included Mary, who did not recognize me at times, but also included Anna, a lady I had come to admire and love.

One morning, weeks later, I pulled my car into a handicapped parking space because I was running late to check on Mary. Sleep had evaded me the night before, and I was unusually tired. After hanging a blue and white handicapped sign from the rearview mirror, I sat for a moment, dreading the torturous day facing me. I pondered the propriety of taking up a space that might be more suited to someone who might really need it. My conscience was eased when I considered that I would be one of the last visitors to leave the facility that evening, and I did not relish the thought of walking to the visitor parking lot alone after dark. "What the hell," I said as I opened the car door.

I never use an umbrella despite the often-rainy weather. They are just too much of a nuisance. That morning, I pulled my jacket close to my neck and walked briskly toward the shelter of the entrance portico, the light rain chilling my sparsely-haired head. An urge to cough reminded me of the effects of my recent two-week bout with something akin to the flu. I opened the door to the lobby, entered, and then stopped to catch my breath.

I pushed the lever on the wall and waited for the double doors to open away from me. Straight ahead was the nurses' station, a semicircle in the center of a larger circle, from which corridors fed, like spokes on a wheel, into separate patient wards and activity rooms. Empty faces of half a dozen patients in wheelchairs, three on each side of the entranceway, prattled to no one in particular. I recognized all of them by sight but knew only one by name, a man of sixty-five or so, his elevated leg heavily bandaged and stretched out from his wheelchair. He took hold of my hand as I attempted to walk by. The man's voice was strong and authoritative, belying his obvious departure from reality. "Do I know you?"

I stopped. "Sure, Dave, you know me. We talked yesterday." *In fact, we talk every day.* "How are you this morning?"

"Not well." He tugged at my hand and raised his voice above the din of the other prattlers and the chatter emanating from the nurses' station. "They need to do something about the portions around here. Have you seen the size of the portions?"

I knew the answer but asked anyway, "What's wrong with them, Dave?"

"They are so small they will starve a pigeon."

"You want me to talk with someone about it?"

"No, I want you to sign my petition."

Just then, Anna pushed her walker through the double doors. "There you are," she said, smiling as she looked in my direction.

Dave shouted at Anna, "Can't you see we are conducting business?"

"Don't raise your voice, young man." Anna continued walking toward me.

Dave moved his wheelchair closer to me while directing his anger at Anna. "Stay out of my business, lady."

Anna held her hands skyward. "May God have mercy on your soul."

I took hold of her hand. It was time to put an end to Dave's aggressive behavior. Giving Dave's shoulder a reassuring touch,

I said, "All right, Dave. Let me know when you have the petition ready." It was the same thing I said to him for the past thirty mornings.

"What are you talking about?" Dave pulled at the bandage on his leg. "My daughter is taking me home today. Where in the hell are the nurses when you need them?"

Anna and I walked back toward the main corridor. "He's a nasty man," she said, "but God will forgive him if he repents."

"I know," I said, but my mind was on Dave, a man no older than I, much too young to have lost touch with reality. He was obviously well-educated. I wondered what his profession was before his brain turned into a dried sponge.

Anna began to hum "Amazing Grace" as we walked casually back to the ward. When we arrived at her room, she looked up at me. "Do you mind if I come with you this morning?"

"Of course not, Anna. You know Mary will be happy to see you."

"Sometimes, I just need to be with somebody. Maybe Marie will come to see me before much longer."

"I spoke with her yesterday. She will be here to see you very soon."

I know that Anna's God forgives little white lies, and I would happily tell another one just to see her dark eyes light up like stars.

Chapter Thirty-Five
DAILY CHORES

Christmas time was approaching, and Mary had spent her first six months at Westwood Convalescent Center with not much hope she would ever leave the facility alive. The first of my daily chores was to visit the center and see to the needs of Mary and Anna. Westwood was considered by many as the premier long-term care facility in Wayne County, Michigan. Even so, the place was understaffed, with employees receiving minimum-wage salaries. They simply did not have the time or motivation to devote to patients' essential needs. I filled in when I could and raised hell when I could not.

After arriving at about nine-thirty each day and caring for Mary's and Anna's unfulfilled needs, I usually took Mary outside for a while, even in bad weather. I wrapped her tightly in multiple blankets, keeping warm while I shivered in the cold. We never missed an opportunity to share these few minutes, especially when the sun was shining.

I was late visiting Mary and was hurrying past Anna's

room. After a half dozen steps beyond her door, I heard her calling me.

"Papa!"

I turned toward her. "Yes, Anna."

"I need to see you."

I walked back to where she stood in the doorway. "How can I help?"

"I can't find my harmonica; someone took it."

"No, Anna, you must have misplaced it. I will help you look for it."

"Now," she said. "I would like to have it now."

"And I would like to hear you play it now. Let me check on Mary and I will come back as soon as I can."

I could tell by the shrug of her shoulders Anna did not like my solution to her problem. She walked to her bedside chair and plopped down with a disgusted look on her face. When she saw me watching her through the doorway, she scowled. "Well, go on and hurry, Papa."

Mary's breakfast tray with uneaten food was sitting on her bedside table. She was usually able to feed herself, but on some mornings the task of eating had become too much for her. It angered me that no one had bothered to check on her since leaving the tray at breakfast, which was usually seven-thirty.

"Where have you been?" she asked. "You just get later and later."

"You're right; I am almost a half hour late. Why didn't you eat your breakfast?"

"I didn't like it."

"What is it?"

"I don't know."

"Want to see what it is?" I lifted the cover over the main dish. "Scrambled eggs and sausage, want some?"

"No," she said. "I'm not hungry."

"Has your diaper been changed this morning?"

"I don't remember."

I pulled back her covers. The odor told me that an aide had not checked on her or changed her since the night before. I turned on the attendant's light and waited.

"How long have you been like this?" I said to Mary.

"I don't know," she replied.

While waiting for the aide to come and take care of Mary, I walked back to Anna's room. She was still seated in the chair.

"It isn't here."

I lifted her pillow and then raised her mattress. "When did you last have your harmonica?"

About that time, Shanika, an aide I knew well, was passing by Anna's room. I stepped into the hallway and called her name. She turned and came back to me.

"Did you take care of Anna this morning?" I asked.

"Yes, I did part of the time. Alisha also helped."

"Her harmonica is missing."

She shook her head and smiled. "I knew it would cause trouble."

"What do you mean."

"Don't tell anyone I told you, but the nurse on duty last night took her harmonica off the nightstand."

"Why in the hell would she do that?"

"She said other patients were trying to sleep."

I turned for the main corridor, arriving at the nurse's station ready to do battle. As I stood looking across the reception desk, I saw a harmonica on a table across the area from me. "Is that Anna's harmonica?"

"I think so," the receptionist said.

"Give it to me," I demanded.

"I can't. The head nurse said she can't play it anymore because other patients are complaining."

"The hell she can't. Most of the other patients don't know they are still in this world. Now give me the damned harmonica or I will come back there and get it."

The attendant handed it to me. "I hope I don't get in trouble."

"If you do, just let me know, and I will take it up with the facility administrator."

After returning the harmonica to Anna, I went back to Mary's room and listened to a wonderful rendition of "Nothing but the Blood of Jesus" coming from Anna's room.

WHEN IT WAS TIME FOR THE NOON MEAL, I CALLED AN aide, and together, we helped Mary into her wheelchair. As we walked toward the cafeteria, I noticed Anna was headed in the same direction, just a few feet ahead of us.

As I got closer to the dining room, I could see Tom, an occasional patient at the facility, already seated alone. As I neared his table, I asked, "Dolly coming to see you today?"

Tom nodded vigorously.

"Need anything, Tom?"

"Where's the food?"

Tom was a retired electrical contractor, probably seventy,

well off but not wealthy. He was on the cusp of the dark abyss, but still agile and at times overly energetic. Dolly, his wife, cared for him at home most of the year because they could not afford full residency at Westwood. She admitted him for a few weeks when her patience and energy were exhausted. Tom had been there for nearly a month and would be going home in a few days. His appetite seemed insatiable, as would probably be demonstrated once again when his meal was served. Dolly was one of the few people at the facility with whom I could hold a reasonable discussion about current events and the news of the day. So, I looked forward to seeing her when she visited Tom.

"The food's coming, Tom. You wait right here with us."

I helped Mary into a chair then sat at the table beside her."

The empty chair next to me was reserved for Dolly, who usually arrived promptly at noon.

Ten minutes later, other residents begin to appear, some on walkers, some in wheelchairs, others unaided. I set about performing self-appointed chores, laying out bibs, and serving milk and fruit juice to arriving diners. I stopped to assist Shirley, a demure little woman of ninety, with her bib.

When she spoke, she paused after each word, her voice trembling. "You're – the – nicest – white – man – I - know." Her huge brown eyes look lovingly at me.

I touched her hand, "You're nice too, Shirley."

She flinched. "Ouh, Ouh," then drew back her hand. "You hurt me."

There was no longer hesitancy in her manner of speech.

"I didn't hurt you, Shirley."

"You do that again and I'll punch you in the belly."

I laughed out loud, imagining the frail little woman

pounding away with her tiny fists on the stomach protruding over my belt. I moved on to the next table where Anna was seated alone.

"Papa, will you get me some placemats? I am having a party today."

"Certainly," I said, knowing Anna often assumed she was hosting guests at her table. I went to the storage rack and returned with four bibs. I placed one on Anna and snapped it on the back of her neck. The other three, I put around the table as placemats. Anna smiled as she sat back in her chair, obviously enjoying the attendees at her party.

The sound of *"Amazing Grace"* being played on her harmonica followed me back to Mary's table. After a few bars, I heard her voice above the noise of the dining room.

"Listen everyone; you are all invited to my party. It is my funeral today."

I walked back to her table and took a seat across from her. "I came to celebrate your birthday, Anna. Isn't it your birthday?"

"Yes," she said, "by the grace of God, it is."

A moment later, Dolly came into the dining room and took a seat next to Tom. I left Anna to celebrate her birthday and went back to have a meaningful conversation with Dolly.

Chapter Thirty-Six
FIRST ANNIVERSARY

A year passed with me spending at least seven hours each day at the convalescent center. I was there so much I began to see myself as a resident and a protector of the two women in my life, my wife, Mary, and my second love, Anna. By then, two roommates of Mary's had passed, replaced by a new person each time two days later. I saw for myself that the aides, nurses, and maintenance personnel became inured to losing patients to the grim reaper. I understood the necessity of adopting such an attitude in order to cope with the loss of people in their care. But each time I witnessed a patient being taken out the side entrance for the last time, I could not resist shedding a tear. I knew that I would, too soon, see Mary and Anna being carried away on a gurney covered by a white sheet. Such thoughts made me all the more determined to ensure their days at Westwood were as comfortable as possible.

During the previous six months, Anna's daughter, Marie, visited twice. Each time, mother and daughter sang duets of Christian songs. I was happy to see that Anna's prayer to God, requesting that her children might be singers, had been answered. They sang behind the closed door to Anna's room. During those sessions, I pushed Mary's wheelchair up and down the hallway, staying in the vicinity of the room where both Mary and I could enjoy the harmony. When the music ended, Marie and I discussed her mother's seemingly boundless energy, belying her age of ninety-seven, rapidly approaching ninety-eight. As sanguine as we were about Anna's health, we both noted a diminishing of memory and ability to hold extended conversations. We acknowledged the end for her would come too soon. However, Anna had other thoughts. She was prepared to meet Jesus when God was ready to call her away, but she still made the best of the days given to her without complaint, just as she had always done.

ANOTHER MORNING FOUND ME IN THE MAIN corridor of Westwood, dreading the day that lay ahead. A bad cough kept me awake much of the previous night, leaving me with a sinus headache I was unable to shake. I turned into the hallway leading to Mary's room. I was reluctant but compelled by my conscience to stop at Room-127 and look in. The old man in the nearest bed was lying on his back; his mouth was open, his body immobile except for the barely discernible movement of his lips.

"Help me, help me, help me, help me."

I wiped away the tears forming in my eyes, thankful to be the one still standing, looking in on the pathetic old man. I turned and walked on down the hallway past Anna's room, vowing not to stop again to hear the old man's misery, the same vow I made the morning before.

Shanika, my favorite aide, was leaving Mary's room. She placed an empty food tray on the cart, looked up, and smiled at me.

"How are you doing this morning, young lady?" I asked.

"The best I can, Mr. Jim, under the circumstances. I just took care of Mary. She is good this morning."

"Thanks, honey," I said. "I don't envy you one little bit."

"You will have to be patient with me today. I hear we will have state inspectors in, and you know we'll be putting on a show." She laughed.

"I will," I said, but was not sure she heard me because by then, she had moved the cart twenty feet down the hallway.

I watched until Shanika reached Anna's room and went in. I knew Anna was also in good hands for the morning.

I got to room 232 and looked in. A curtain was drawn around the bed nearest the door. The stench told me that, behind the curtain, an aide was changing the colostomy bag for Bertha, Mary's latest roommate. I waited until the curtain was opened and saw that Emma, another conscientious aide, was performing the unpleasant chore. She looked up at me, pinched her nose, and smiled, her brilliant white teeth contrasting with her caramel complexion. I walked into the room. A stifling odor lingered like slow settling fog. I held my breath until I could reach the hallway, where I stood for three or four minutes, taking in fresh air.

When Emma emerged from the room, I said, "Honey, you deserve a Purple Heart for that and maybe a medal for bravery."

"All in a day's work, Mr. Jim," she said. "Oh, yes, I sprayed the room. It ain't so bad now." She pushed her cart to the next room where I heard her greet the occupant with her usual cheerful attitude, "Good morning, Charlie. You okay this morning?"

I thought to myself: *God, let me be more understanding and appreciative of all I have, and let me be grateful to people who do these demeaning chores.*

Mary was dressed in the slacks and blouse I set out for her the previous evening, sitting in her wheelchair by the bed, her attention fastened on the television, watching a rerun of Family Feud. I knew the twenty dollars I slipped to Shanika and Emma each week was paying off, ensuring that Mary was cleaned, diapered, and dressed by the time I arrived each morning. Sometimes that did not happen if Emma and Shanika were not on duty.

"How are you this morning, honey?" I asked.

Her blue eyes lit up. "Where've you been? You're late again."

"You're imagining things. I'm right on time."

She gestured at the clock on the wall. "Ten o'clock. That's not on time."

I kissed her cheek. "Look again, honey. It's only nine; I'm early today."

"Seems later," she said. "Do you want to go outside?" She smiled coyly.

"No," I teased, "I don't want to go. Do you?"

"Yes, but I have to be changed first." She rolled her eyes. I took it as an apology.

"Haven't you already gone this morning?"

"Yep."

"You've gone again?"

"Yep."

"Number one or number two?"

"Number two."

Damn. I turned on the light for assistance and took a seat, leaning my chair against the wall. I closed my eyes for a moment, wishing I had slept well the previous night, knowing I would not be able to sleep any better this night.

"You mad at me?" Her voice was close to a whisper.

Mary's question caused me to open my eyes. "Of course not." I touched her hand to reassure her. "Just tired."

Twenty minutes later, Shanika showed up, pushing the patient lift. "I'm sorry, Mr. Jim. I saw your light but had to wait for a hoist."

Together, we rolled the hoist into place and lifted Mary onto her bed. I left the room while Shanika cleaned Mary and changed her diaper. I stood by the door, taking a deep breath, savoring a moment in the day that belonged only to me. Minutes later, I heard Shanika calling, "Mr. Jim, you ready to help me lift Miss Mary out of bed?"

At that moment, Peggy passed by the door in her wheelchair. She looked neither right nor left. "Mama ... Mama ... Mama ... Mama." At the end of the hallway, she turned into the main corridor, her pleas fading, absorbed into the sounds of attendants hurrying to and from patients' rooms and the noises emanating from the kitchen where lunch was being prepared.

I pushed Mary outdoors through a side entrance. We huddle under a canopy, taking shelter from the blazing sun of late August. It was going to be a hot, muggy day. Rain had poured down for the past three days, and the humidity was still unbearable. It was much more tolerable than the bitter winter days that had lingered into April. My attention was diverted to a gray hearse parked at the curb. An attendant came outside, pulling a gurney covered with a white sheet. By the attendant's casual pace, I knew the person on the gurney would not be returning to Westwood Convalescent Center.

After the hearse pulled away, I made a show of checking my watch. "Time for lunch. We better go."

Mary didn't answer right away, then looking up at me, said, "Yes, let's go. I'm hungry too."

We took our seats in the dining room and waited for the food to be served. I looked at Anna's usual table. She had not yet arrived. After a few minutes, I said to Mary, "I better go check on Anna."

I walked back down the main corridor and then checked her room. She was not there. I thought of the aquarium, the one place where she found profound peace. Halfway to the patients' lounge, I saw her coming in my direction.

"Where have you been, Anna? Do you know it is lunchtime?"

"What's that?"

"You know what that is." I walked with her, directing her toward the dining room.

"Did you know that the big goldfish is missing?"

"No," I said. "What do you think happened to it?"

"It must be dead."

"Do you want me to find out?"

"Yes. I think it is in Heaven, don't you?"

"Maybe," I said.

As we passed Room-127, the door was ajar. I pushed it further open and looked in. The old man's bed was empty. I said nothing to Anna as we resumed walking toward the dining room.

Chapter Thirty-Seven

THE STATE INSPECTION

Everyone, even inspectors, has a purpose in life. In the case of the nursing homes and convalescent centers, their purpose is to ensure patients are cared for humanely, as required by the state. When they inspect, we know, and the inspectors know, they are not looking at a normal day's performance by the staff and aides. It isn't that they attempt to deceive, but they certainly put their best foot forward when they are hosting the state inspectors for an entire day.

You might wonder, as I did, what happens when the state springs a surprise inspection on the facility. It is my unconfirmed opinion that someone at the state level always tips off management just in the nick of time. And the scrambling begins to make everything appear to be humming right along without a glitch. Repairs to equipment, inoperable since the last inspection are made; the beds are all fitted with clean linen; the patients are bathed; the meals, especially the noon meals, to be sampled by inspectors, are sumptuous by normal standards; and the posted menu for the week is made to indicate that all meals are similarly prepared and just as nutritious.

Shanika's information was confirmed when I saw an oversized lady prowling the halls and main corridor, clipboard in hand. I recognized her from an inspection she and three others conducted two months earlier, but she obviously did not recall meeting me then. She spoke as I rounded the corner into the long-term patients' hallway.

"Good morning," she said.

"Morning." I stopped directly in front of Anna's door, which was closed.

"Are you a visitor or staff?"

"Well, to be honest, I feel like a permanent resident, but I am here to spend time with my wife and the lady who lives right here." I turned my head toward Anna's door and pointed to the nameplate that read *Anna Marie Gamble*.

"Oh, yes, I recall her. Someone in the front office told me she is the oldest person in long-term residence here."

"Then I must be the youngest." I joked.

"No," she said, rifling through the papers on her clipboard. "According to the roster, that would be Mary Morris. She's just sixty-two."

"That is my wife."

"I'm sorry," the lady said. "I hope she is doing well."

"She's getting by, probably doing better than I anticipated when she came here more than a year ago. "

"I will want to speak with her later if you don't mind."

"Of course not," I said. "She has her good and bad days. If she is coherent, we will be happy to answer your questions."

Just then, I heard Anna blowing on her harmonica, up and down the scale, ending with "Pop Goes the Weasel."

The lady looked surprised. "What is that?"

I laughed. The oldest person here is playing her harmonica. She is doing well also, better than anyone, but she might have expected.

The lady moved down the corridor, writing notations on the clipboard.

The words "long-term" played in my mind. They were nothing more than euphemisms for "leaving on a gurney." I stood without moving until that terrible thought ran its course, then I knocked on Anna's door, cracked it, then walked in. Anna was sitting by her bed weeping.

"Why are you crying, Anna?"

"I was just thinking of George. He has not been here to see me in such a long time. I think he has forgotten me."

"Oh, no," I said. "I heard from him. He said he will come to see you soon."

"When?"

"Soon. Would you like a candy bar?"

Her eyes lit up. She rose from her chair and held out her hand.

I reached into my pocket and handed her a Snickers, her favorite chocolate delight.

"Here," I said, "but you must play " "This Train is Bound for Glory" after you eat it."

She took the candy and sat down.

"I will check on you before lunch, okay?"

Her mouth was full of chocolate. She nodded her head.

I hurried toward Mary's room, knowing I would be

chastised for my tardiness. When I arrived, a state inspector was sitting near Mary's wheelchair. They were carrying on a conversation as if the two of them had known each other all their lives.

I stood in the doorway, waiting for the inspector to complete her questionnaire. A harmonica rendition of "This Train is Bound for Glory" filled the hallway.

AFTER THE INSPECTOR LEFT, MARY AND I SPENT HALF an hour outside, then went to the therapy room for her daily exercise, which usually lasted about an hour. When the therapy ended, it was time to prepare for the noon meal. I pushed the wheelchair to her room, where she washed her face and hands before lunch.

When we reached the dining room, Anna was seated alone at her usual table. Tom's month of residency had expired at the end of July, so Dolly and he would not be at our table. Knowing the inspectors would observe the meal. I led Anna to our table, where I could shield her from their questions.

"Papa," she said, "Did you know I am going to Owego tomorrow?

"No. You didn't tell me. How are you going?"

"I'm walking. It isn't far. I do it all the time. Usually, I just walk through the woods. Of course, I stop and spend time talking to Jesus along the way. He is always with me when I walk in the wilderness."

"Maybe I will go with you."

She laughed. "You can't walk that far."

More residents were arriving for lunch. An attendant pushed Jewel to a table across the room from us. His demeanor was in direct contrast with that of Garth, a grizzled sixty-three-year-old who thrived on his own mischief. He trailed the attendant pushing Jewel, holding onto the sash from her scrubs. He seated himself next to Jewel.

"What's for lunch?" Garth demanded from no one in particular.

"Read the menu," a man near the kitchen said as if he had control of all his mental faculties.

"Who the hell asked you?" Garth got up from his chair. "I'll kick your ass."

"Sit down, please," Anna said without raising her voice. "Would someone please get me some milk?"

Two inspectors took seats at the tables where patients sat. The food cart was pushed to the center of the dining room from where the aides distributed trays.

"Hmm, baked chicken, mashed potatoes, and green peas," one of the inspectors commented. "Looks good."

"And plenty of it," an aide said.

Carter, a toothless man from Harlan, Kentucky, took a seat at the table where Jewel and Garth were seated. As always, he talked of his days on the farm when he was a boy. "Give them cows hay." As he spoke, spittle flew in all directions with every word. "And save some for them horses."

"Shut the hell up." Garth pushed Carter's shoulder.

"Help me. I'm falling. I'm going to break my neck."

Garth laughed. "I hope you fall, and I hope you break your neck."

An attendant, who was setting trays in front of patients,

moved between Garth and Carter. She placed their food trays on the table. Both men begin eating. Then she unwrapped a sandwich and set it before Jewel.

"What kind of sandwich is that?" Garth asked.

"Ham," the attendant said.

"How does he rate?" Garth demanded. He reached for the sandwich, took a bite, and put the sandwich back on the table. "You won't like it," he said to Jewel.

By then, all patients had been served. Anna stood and clinked her spoon against a cup.

"Everyone, listen."

The chatter didn't stop.

She said again, this time a little louder, "Listen, everyone. I just want to thank you all for coming to my birthday party."

She remained standing as she removed a harmonica from her pocket and played some bars of Amazing Grace. She stopped abruptly and sat down.

I touched her hand. She withdrew from me, appearing confused and disoriented, more than I had witnessed in her before. After Mary finished her meal, we stayed with Anna while she ate bits and pieces of the food on her plate, stopping after each bite to bow her head and mouth the words, "Thank you, Jesus."

'Don't you think you should eat something more?" I asked Anna.

"How old are you?" she asked.

"You know how old I am, Anna. I've told you before, more than once."

She regained her bearings, her manner of speech exhibiting

strength. "When you get to be a hundred, you can tell me what to do."

"All right, Anna."

"Anna, Anna, Anna; that's all I hear. I'm just going to change my name."

Sarah, a quiet little woman in her late eighties, got up. She knocked over cups of juice from an adjacent table as she rose from her seat. The aides scrambled to clean the table and set out new drinks for the four people seated there. Sarah wandered to the window and looked out. The sun was shining brightly, but hidden by a large oak tree, casting a shadow on the window Sarah was looking through. She turned to the people still seated. "Has anyone noticed how it gets dark every night?"

One of the aides helped her back to her table and directed her attention to the uneaten food on the plate in front of her.

"What's that," she asked.

"Chicken and mashed potatoes," the aide responded.

"I don't like it," Sarah said.

"Would you like Italian sausage instead?"

"I think so."

The aide carried a new tray to Sarah's table and lifted the cover from the plate. Garth, seated at an adjacent table, began to laugh.

"What's so funny?" Sarah acted offended.

Garth stood and pointed to the sausage. "That looks like what I have in my pants." He chortled, slapping both arms against his sides.

Sarah pushed away her plate. "I'm not hungry."

Peggy wheeled her chair, with a baby tray attached to the front, into the dining room. She paddled rapidly toward Jewel, ramming against his table, sending cups of juice tumbling onto the floor. She backed away, then went forward, crashing into another table, spilling more water, milk, and juice. As the liquids dripped onto the floor, an attendant took control of Peggy's chair, pushing it against the wall. Another attendant hurried to clean the spills. After cleanup, service continued with empty trays being retrieved by the aides.

Garth spied the piece of cake on Jewel's tray. "Why is his cake bigger than mine?"

"They're the same," an attendant replied, aggravation evident despite the smile she exhibited.

"No. It's bigger." Garth stood and reached for Jewel's cake.

"Damn," the attendant said almost under her breath. She snatched the dessert plate from Garth's table and swapped it with Jewel's plate.

Garth eyed the size of his new portion, smiled, took a bite, and spit it out. "Who baked this crap?"

Alisha brought a cup of water to Peggy and set it on her tray. Peggy pushed the cup onto the floor, splashing water onto half a dozen diners, all of whom scolded her vehemently. She turned her wheelchair around and paddled into the corridor, leaving behind a trail of destruction. Just at that moment, two more inspectors entered and meandered through the lunchroom, asking questions of patients as they passed. With order restored, trays were collected from the remaining tables. The attendants doted over the diners, cajoling and joking with those who were alert enough to participate. I shook my head, doing my best not to laugh, wondering how the inspectors might describe what they had just witnessed.

Chapter Thirty-Eight

ANNA TURNS ONE HUNDRED

All of the management and staff anticipated Anna's one-hundredth birthday, which was rapidly approaching in August 2018. By then, she had been at the facility for eight years, defying her anticipated passing, year after year. I had hopes for Anna's longevity because of her positive outlook on life. She seemed to persevere happily through every adversity. She still had her good days and bad days but always endured most of them with an outward optimism, taking solace in her songs of praise played on her harmonica.

I wish I could have had the same feelings about Mary, whose mind frequently wandered in and out of reality. Her mental instability was complicated by a diagnosed heart condition. Her physical activity was restricted to visits to an area by the nurse's station where immobile patients sat in chairs and batted about large balloons with apparent delight, the extent of their daily exertion. Anna would participate for short periods until her mind was diverted by some thought from her past, giving her cause to get out of her seat and wander toward the aquarium. After the play sessions ended, I would return Mary to her room, call her aide, then go find Anna.

One afternoon, I followed Anna to the aquarium, where she was standing with her nose against the tank. I startled her when I called her name.

"Anna, are you okay?"

She put a finger to her lips. "Shhh. You'll scare the fish."

"They can't hear me."

"Yes, they can." She pointed to a fish swimming in the furthest corner from her. "George can hear you."

"Is that George?"

She scoffed. "Not my George, but that's what I named that fish because he is so sweet."

She backed away from the tank, walked over to a chair, and sat. By the time I was seated beside her, she was blowing on her harmonica. She played most of "Ave Maria," stopped suddenly, and put the harmonica into her pocket.

From behind the fish tank, someone clapped. I peered around to see a man I knew only as Walter—a man of about seventy. He was making his weekly visit to spend time with his mother, whom I assumed to be past ninety. There was resignation in his voice as he quietly, gently answered the same questions she asked every week.

"What's your name?"

"Walter."

"Do I know you?"

"I'm your son."

"My son?

"Yes, Mother"

"How long have I been here?"

"Five years." He touched her arm.

"Eat something, Mother." He held out a sandwich.

She took a bite, maybe a second one, and then looked with empty eyes at her son. "What's your name?"

"Walter."

"Do you work?"

"No, I'm retired."

"What did you do?"

"I was an architect."

"What's that?"

"I did drawings and designed buildings."

"How long have I been here?"

"Five years."

"Five years? I must like it then."

I got up to leave and helped Anna from her seat. Walter's eyes met mine. The two of us exchanged empathetic grimaces. Walter resumed his circular discussion with his mother. My attention was returned to Anna. I coaxed her to go with me back to her room.

As we walked, she spoke of her forthcoming birthday. "I will have a birthday soon. Are you coming to my party?"

"Of course I am. Everyone is coming."

"George is coming." She stopped walking and then turned back toward the lounge and aquarium.

"No, Anna," I said, "it is almost dinner time. You need to get ready."

"I was going to look for George."

I took hold of her walker. "I think George is still in Owego."

She sighed, intently grasping the handles of her walker. "Probably," she said.

We continued up the hallway. When we reached her room, I turned on the light for an aide. "When it's dinner time, I will walk with you."

Mary was still in her wheelchair, needing to be changed before the evening meal. I turned on the call light and waited. I was resigned to my inevitable duties, reaching deep for the patience I would need to get through the remainder of the day. I yawned, then let go of an involuntary sigh. Grim-faced, I had not spoken to Mary since returning to the room.

She looked up, her eyes glistening with the makings of tears. "You mad at me?"

"Of course not," I said, but I wasn't sure of my feelings at that moment. It was 4:00 p.m., and I had to persevere until after the evening meal and ensure Mary and Anna were properly prepared for the night.

THE NEXT MORNING, FIRST THING, I WENT TO THE administration office and spoke with Joanne, the assistant administrator. "You know Anna's one-hundredth birthday is only three days away, don't you?"

"Yes, of course, and we will have a nice celebration for her in the dining room at the noon meal. It isn't often we have someone turning one hundred."

Something caustic came to mind, but instead, I said, "What can I do to help? I thought I might get her a cake."

"That would be nice," Joanne said. "Her daughter called. She will be here."

"You mean Marie?"

"Yes. Do you know her? She might intend to bring a cake."

"I know her and her husband, Frank. I'll give them a call and let them know I will have a cake for Anna."

"By the way, Sheila and Joe will be here to play, especially for Anna. I know you are friends with them."

Sheila and Joe were a music duo from a nearby Michigan town. They were nationally known and performed frequently at the Westwood Convalescence Center. They often dedicated songs to Mary and me. Anna sang and played her harmonica with them a few times in the past, but I doubted her ability to do so at the age of one hundred. I would not have been surprised if she would prove me wrong.

I BROUGHT A LARGE SHEET CAKE, ENOUGH TO FEED the thirty or so people expected at the noon meal the following Thursday. The words "Happy One Hundred, Anna," in red, her favorite color, was sprawled across the two-foot-long cake. A six-inch single candle sat on a corner, surrounded by a large rhinestone tiara.

The staff set Anna's table in the center of the dining room with her daughter and Frank. Mary and I were at a table nearby. Sheila and Joe played softly as meals of hamburgers, and fries were served. After the meal, Sheila began a rendition of "Happy Birthday, Anna."

As the music played, Marie cut her mother's cake, giving

the first piece to Anna. A container of vanilla ice cream was placed on each table.

A few gifts remained to be opened by Anna. The first was a Bible from Mary and me. Marie and Frank gave her clothing as they did with each visit to the facility. Other patients, capable of understanding the event, joined in the singing and wished her a happy birthday.

Sheila invited Anna to perform a duet of "Amazing Grace," but by then, Anna's mind had taken her to other places. She stood, clinked her spoon against a glass, and said the same words she had spoken at mealtimes a dozen times before.

"I want to thank all of you for coming to my birthday party."

All the staff clapped and shouted: "Happy Birthday, Anna."

She sat back down and looked about the room as if she were among a crowd of strangers. Marie and Frank collected her gifts. Together, they walked to her room.

As I pushed Mary's wheelchair past Anna's door, I heard Marie and Anna singing "Nothing but the Blood of Jesus."

Chapter Thirty-Nine

ANNA IS GONE

Friday morning following Anna's birthday party, I came to the facility early because I made appointments with a hairdresser for Mary and Anna, Mary's at nine o'clock, and Anna's at ten. When I approached Anna's room, I saw a gurney covered by a white sheet being moved through the doorway. My first thought was, *Thank God she had a good day yesterday.*

The grim-faced attendant pushed the gurney by me without speaking. When he was five feet past me, I asked, "Is that Anna?"

He shook his head. "No. It's her roommate, Mrs. Fleischman. Anna is fine. That old lady will outlive us all."

I went through Anna's door without knocking. She sat with her elbows on her bed, eyes closed in prayer. "Thank you, Jesus, for taking Vera home to be with you."

"And thank God, you're alright, Anna."

It occurred to me that Vera Fleischman was Jewish, but I supposed that after Anna's prayer, Jesus would intervene on her behalf and would welcome her into Heaven. Vera was ninety-two and had outlived all expectations. To my knowledge, no one ever visited her at the facility. She was another ward of the state, now gone to a better place. I knew that by the next day, another poor soul would take her place as Anna's roommate.

The aide was taking away the breakfast tray when I got to Mary's room. She was dressed and looking alert, more so than I had seen for the past week. I wheeled her to the beauty shop and waited for the hairdresser to arrive. I dared not tell Mary of the death of Anna's roommate, even though she might not comprehend what I would say to her.

Minutes after the hairdresser began washing Mary's hair, alarms sounded throughout the facility, signaling that one of the exits had been breached by a patient. The alarm always sent the attendants scrambling to see which door was opened and what patient might be missing. That person was usually a man by the name of Salvador. Although he was well enough to walk unaided, he roamed the halls in a wheelchair. Each time the alarm went off, the administrator, nurses, and aides wasted no time getting to the exits, even though they all probably assumed Salvador was escaping again. Fifteen minutes later, an announcement was made that Salvador was back in his room, and all patients were accounted for.

When Mary's hair was done, I pushed her back to the room and went to get Anna for her appointment. I knocked on the door and then entered. Anna was gone. My instinct was to check for her in the patient lounge by the fish tank, but there was no sign of her there.

I ran up the hallway and down the main corridor to the front desk. "Have you seen Anna this morning?"

The attendants did not seem to be alarmed. "She hasn't been here yet. Did you check the aquarium?"

"Yes. She's missing. We need to check the grounds to see if she went outside with Salvador. Maybe he saw her. What is his room number?"

After an eternal minute, one of the nurses' aides responded. "Room 123."

"Well, sound the damn alarm," I said. "I'm sure she has left the building."

Someone behind the counter sounded the alarm, and people scrambled again, some of them cursing Salvador as they ran down the hallways to check the exits.

"Don't you think we should notify the police to begin looking for her outside?"

"She couldn't go far," the aide said.

"How in the hell do you know? She's probably been gone for more than an hour. You don't know Anna if you think she can't do what she wants to do."

An aide dialed 911 and reported that one of our patients may have wandered into a nearby neighborhood.

I ran to room 123. Salvador was watching television.

"Did Anna follow you outside?"

"Who is that?"

"You know Anna, damn it. Did she go outside when you did?"

He didn't take his eyes off the TV screen. "Someone did. It may have been Anna. Was she on a walker?"

"Which door did you go out?"

He pointed over his shoulder in the general direction of the door at the end of ward 200. I ran to the door and opened it, causing the alarm to sound once again. A few feet away, I saw Anna's abandoned walker. All sorts of dark possibilities flooded my mind. I assumed the walker was too difficult to push in the tall grass.

Near a main intersecting street was a paved walking trail. Sometimes, patients propelled their wheelchairs there. The more agile patients walked to the nearby trail. In her early years at the facility, she walked that trail for short distances. Since she was no longer as agile as then, I doubted her ability to walk that far without assistance, but I ran to the beginning of the trail to see if she defied my expectations again.

Police cars, with blue lights flashing, patrolled the nearby streets. Dreading the prospect that something terrible had happened to Anna, I returned to retrieve her walker and wait for the bad news. I took a last look in all directions before giving up completely, dreading the phone call I would have to make to Marie, notifying her of her mother's disappearance.

A clump of bushes lay a hundred feet or so away from her abandoned walker. I hurried in that direction. Hidden by the bushes, Anna knelt by a large boulder. I approached her, saying nothing until she turned in my direction.

"There you are," she said.

"What are you doing, Anna?"

"Praying,"

"Why didn't you pray in your room or at the aquarium?"

"God told me to come here."

"Have you finished praying?"

"Yes. Let's go now."

"Where are we going?"

"Owego," she said resolutely.

"May I go with you?"

"If you want to."

"Alright," I said, taking her by the hand.

She didn't speak as I led her back to the door, where she had abandoned her walker, and neither did I.

Once inside the building, I said, "The hairdresser is waiting to make you look beautiful."

"I am already beautiful in the eyes of God," she said.

We walked together for a few minutes before I spoke. "You're beautiful in my eyes too, Anna."

Chapter Forty

MORE AGGRAVATION

Mary was scheduled for therapy at 4:00 p.m. I wheeled her down the hall into the main corridor, arriving promptly at her appointed time. The door to the therapy room was locked. I waited impatiently for several minutes before pushing her back to the attendants' station. I leaned over the counter and looked at a nurse's aide, who was busy at her desk. "The therapy room is locked. Where's Marion?"

The attendant looked up from her computer. "I think she left a note for you." She rifled through a basket on the workstation next to hers. "Here it is." She handed me a folded sheet of paper.

I read the note, knowing my face was growing flush with anger. "What does she mean, all therapy time is used up for the month?'"

"I don't know, Jim. You need to take that up with her."

"We've been over this more than once. I thought it was resolved."

"I don't know anything about it. I just happened to see the note when I came on today."

I said the same thing I had grown accustomed to saying. "I know it isn't your fault." I thought about leaving, but the note stuck in my craw. I turned back to the counter. "But it's somebody's fault, Janet, and I mean to find out whose."

It was an hour before dinner time. Mary and I went down the corridor, stopping at the dining room to greet Dolly, seated at a table watching television. I stepped into the archway and asked. "Where's Tom?"

"Sleeping," Dolly said. "He was nodding in his chair, so I had the aide put him back into bed. Thought I would rest a few minutes before dinner is served."

"See you at dinner," I said.

I continued pushing Mary down the corridor. I stopped at Anna's door, knocked, and entered. Anna was lying on her bed, apparently sleeping. As I turned to tiptoe out, I heard her say, "That you, Papa?"

"Yes, Anna. It will be dinner time soon. Do you want me to help you wash up?"

"I'm not helpless yet," she retorted.

"I know, dear. I just wanted to let you know you can walk with us to the dining room if you want to."

I started back up the hallway, pushing Mary's chair. She turned her head to see my face. "Can we go outside for a few minutes before dinner?"

"Why not?" I said, but all I really wished to do was to sit down and close my eyes.

After twenty minutes outside, I checked my watch. "Better

get going. Anna will be heading for the dining room soon. I
told her we would walk with her."

Bertha, Mary's roommate, was using the bathroom and
had parked her wheelchair by the bathroom door, blocking
access to Mary's bed. I bit my lip, silently searching for a
renewal of endurance, which was rapidly dissipating. I waited a
few minutes, then knocked lightly on the door.

"Are you okay, Bertha?"

"Yes." Her voice was muffled.

I put my mouth close to the door. "I need to move your
chair for a minute."

"No," she responded, "I'm coming right out."

I looked at my watch, checking it minute by minute.
"Hell." I grasped the handles of the chair and pushed it aside.
Bertha opened the bathroom door as I was returning the chair
to its previous spot.

"Why did you move my chair?"

"I'm sorry, Bertha, but I needed to get Mary by her bed so
she can get changed before dinner."

Bertha was still standing in the doorway. "I told you not to
move my chair."

"You have it now. Can I help you get into it?"

"No." She turned about, face flushed with anger, and
dropped into the seat. "I'm going to report you." She backed
the chair away from the bathroom door and wheeled into the
hallway. Looking back, she waved a forefinger in my direction
and then disappeared toward the main corridor.

I turned on the light signaling for an attendant, knowing it
would be several minutes before anyone showed up. I took a
moment to relax, fighting exhaustion and irritability. It would

be at least eight more hours before I could lie down for the night. Neither Mary nor I spoke. Seconds passed. I thought I should say something, but the right words just would not come to mind. It was one of my rare moments bordering on self-pity. Slowly, guilt took over as it occurred to me how much Mary loved me. If our roles were reversed, she would have been by my side every moment of the day. This realization caused me to open my eyes, look lovingly at her, and smile.

"You tired, honey?' she asks.

"I'm fine." I reflected on those words. They had been my mantra all through life. *I'm fine.* No matter the circumstances, I managed to get through them by refusing to quit when others might have. I remembered my boyhood days, growing up poorer than my schoolmates, somehow hiding feelings of inferiority that always burdened me. I recalled nights searching barrooms and beer joints to find my father while my mother stood by the kitchen window at home, watching, waiting, and crying. I'm fine. I thought of my father, in excruciating pain, as he lay dying of *black lung disease* at forty-two. As the eldest son, it was my presumed responsibility to care for Dad to the end.

Mary broke the silence. "You feel okay?"

"I'm fine," I said.

We walked a few feet behind Anna to the dining room. Halfway there, she stopped and waited for us to catch up. "I thought you forgot about me, so I came by myself."

"You know I couldn't do that, Anna."

"I know," she said, "you love me too much."

I would have hugged her, but I feared she would kick my shins.

A s Christmas 2020 approached, I was thankful for Mary's endurance in relative comfort, my continuing good health, and the laborious and tedious tasks performed by the attendants for her during six years of residency at Westwood.

Anna celebrated her 102nd birthday that year and over ten years as a patient at the convalescent center. I doubted that either Mary or Anna comprehended the length of their stays or that the beginning of another year of mere existence for them was right around the corner.

Anna was still spry and alert for short durations, lapsing into cognizant disorientation at times. She ate less and less of her food servings, sometimes not eating at all. Her visits to the aquarium were less frequent, but that is where I could find her if she wasn't in her room when I visited. She participated in the minimal exercises with other patients three times each week but grew impatient after short periods of batting a balloon about the room. I encouraged her to participate in the group. I was usually there to observe her activities. When she took to her walker and meandered down the corridor, I followed at a distance. I think she knew when I was watching, but she never looked back to see if I was there.

Mary could no longer sit erect in her wheelchair without being strapped into an upright position. There were times when she was unaware of her surroundings but was usually capable of coherent conversations for short periods. Because she always loved to be taken outside, I did so for a few minutes every day.

I pulled back Mary's curtain and peered out. "If the sun continues to shine this afternoon, I will take you outside for a little while." My promise brought a much-needed smile to her face.

I turned on the light for an attendant and waited. A half-hour later, Jordan, a young man built like a weightlifter, arrived with a hoist, changed Mary's diaper, and lifted her onto her wheelchair.

"She has to be strapped in," I said.

"I know." He gave me a look that could kill, and I was not about to argue with him. He finished his task and pushed the hoist out the door without speaking.

"You got a burr in your saddle, Jordan?"

He turned and spoke. "Sorry, Jim. This is my seventeenth hour on this ward since yesterday. I am one tired s.o.b."

"Can't blame you," I said as he continued down the hallway.

Freezing rain began about 2:00 p.m. damping my hopes for a few minutes outside with Mary. But by 3:00, the rain changed to small pellets of frozen snow, hominy grits covering small patches of grass here and there. Most of the snow melted almost as quickly as it landed.

"It's snowing," I said as I wrapped Mary like an Eskimo.

"Where are we going?"

"Outside like I promised."

We took shelter under a canopy and watched the snowfall. A gust of wet wind caused me to shudder. I pulled my jacket tighter about me.

"Zip your coat," Mary said, "and where are your gloves?"

"In the car. We'll only be out here a couple of minutes longer."

After two minutes or less, Mary said, "Let's go inside. I'm cold too."

But I knew it was my comfort she was concerned about, not hers.

When we returned to the room, Bertha was in her bed, reading a book. She dropped it and smiled like a long-lost cousin. "Do you have anything to snack on? I'm starved." Apparently, she had forgiven me for the incident involving her wheelchair.

"Sure." I opened a drawer in the bedside stand. "We have oatmeal cakes and peanut butter crackers; let's see. Want some chips?"

"No. Do you have anything in the fridge?"

"Some ham and cheese; how about grapes?"

She nodded.

I placed a handful of grapes and some cheddar cheese on a paper plate.

Bertha began to eat, turned on her television, and elevated the volume.

I asked, "Bertha, can you turn your TV down a little."

"Why do you always complain?" She continued to eat, her eyes fastened on the television.

I shook my head in disbelief, dropped into a chair, leaned back against the wall, and winked at Mary, sitting aghast in her chair.

She mouthed, "She's a nasty person."

I put my finger to my lips. "She can't help it."

Anna pushed her walker into the room as Bertha finished her plate of snacks. She looked about, not speaking.

"Are you lost, Anna?" I asked.

"No." She looked away, slowly turning back to face me. "I'm just inspecting,"

"Well, what do you think?" I played along.

She eyed Bertha's plate holding the remains of her snack. "I think I would like some cheese and crackers."

"Will that help me pass inspection?"

"Maybe." She took the plate, stood for several minutes munching, then walked closer to Mary. "You always look so pretty." She pointed at me. "Why do you have this old man with you?"

Before I could object, she continued, "No, you're really a young man. Just be sure to eat your vegetables." She put the last bit of cracker into her mouth and eased her walker toward the door.

"Where are you headed now, Anna?" I am sure my fondness for the old woman was evident in my voice.

"To Owego. It's been so long since I was there. I'll bet George is worried about me."

"Let me know when you get back."

"I will," she said, "if I ever get back."

As I sat by Mary's bed, the sounds of Anna's harmonica, playing "Amazing Grace, "wafted through the hallway. I cannot say why, but the words she wrote in her memoir came back to me—a reminder of what she endured as a child and the obstacles she overcame to become so accomplished. As forthcoming as her memoir was, there were cruelties in her life that she could not bear to reveal because she did not wish to dishonor her mother and father.

"They are best left in the past," she said.

She played her harmonica for a long period, more than usual, finishing with "This Train is Bound for Glory", her father's favorite song.

I thought about how certain she was of her final destination, and when the train reached glory, she would greet the angels with a harmonica solo of "It is Well with My Soul," ending with "Pop Goes the Weasel."

AFTER DINNER, I WAITED FOR THE ATTENDANT TO prepare Mary for the night. I was happy to see that Emma was on for the evening. She straightened Mary's bed and washed her for the night as I waited by the door. She called me when she was finished.

"Mr. Jim, you want to help me put Mary in bed?

"Sure." I helped Emma put Mary into the hoist and move her over her bed. When she was settled in, I noticed no sound was coming from behind the curtain around Bertha's bed. I pulled back a bit of the curtain to look. A dinner tray was still on the bedside table. The food was untouched. I called Bertha's name. She did not respond. I touched her hand. When she did not object, I realized she was no longer in our world.

I closed the curtain and said nothing until I got to the door. Motioning for Emma to follow, I stepped outside the room.

"Call the nurse. I think Bertha is dead."

Emma moved away from me and dialed her cell phone. Her conversation with someone at the nurse's station was out of my earshot, and I was glad Mary couldn't hear. I hoped she would fall asleep before her roommate was taken out on a gurney, as are most patients in the long-term care ward eventually.

To my knowledge, Bertha never had visitors. I assumed she was a total ward of the state and would have no mourners. A long evening lay ahead of me as I stood at the door, thinking how sad it was to end our lives unloved and unwanted. I would stay until her body was taken away; it was the least I could do.

As Emma went down the hallway and turned into Anna's room, I thought, *That stubborn little lady might outlive all of us even though she is more prepared to go than anyone else in Westwood.*

Chapter Forty-Two

A NEW ROOMMATE

Under the effects of a sleeping pill, Mary slept through the night. When she awoke, the curtains were still drawn around Bertha's bed, which was now empty. After breakfast, she whispered to me.

"Isn't Bertha talking to us today?"

"They sent her home last night," I said. "I think they are moving her to another facility. She wasn't very happy here."

Bertha was the third person to die in a bed across the room from Mary. Sooner or later, she would learn the truth, but I needed to shield her fragility for the moment. Her inability to sit upright or to stand unassisted was wearing her down. She frequently expressed fears of passing and leaving me behind. When a roommate died, Mary was devastated for days. The loss of Bertha to death would be difficult for Mary even though their relationship was contentious much of the time. For the moment, she would know nothing more than I had already revealed. I should have known I couldn't keep it from her very long.

An aide told her the truth before the day ended, and Mary wept, recalling the few times they shared stories of their families when neither an aide nor I was present.

"She wasn't all bad," Mary said.

"No one is," I commented.

"I think she just felt unloved, don't you?"

"Maybe."

I pulled my handkerchief from my pocket and wiped Mary's eyes.

"I'll be next," she said.

I kissed her cheek. "I hope not, honey."

Two days later, I learned that the manager planned to move an elderly lady by the name of Elizabeth Gross into the room with Mary. I knew Lizzy, as we called her. Like Anna, Lizzy was in her eleventh year of residency. But the similarities ended there.

I recalled that four years earlier, Lizzy was active and could carry on intellectual conversations, evidencing her formal education and vocation as an English teacher. She stopped eating her meals in the dining room two years before Bertha passed. I inquired about her health often enough to know she was no longer capable of communicating in any manner and was currently in a near-comatose state.

When the aides came to prepare the bed across from Mary, I asked Shanika who was being moved in.

"You know the lady," she said. "She was a librarian."

"What's her name?"

"Elizabeth Gross, I think."

"No, that lady was a teacher and is not expected to live much longer."

"That's the lady," she said.

I went to the main office and knocked on the administrator's door. We were well acquainted because I often brought my complaints about Mary's and Anna's care to his attention.

He did not appear surprised to see me. "I'll bet you're here about us moving in Elizabeth Gross to room with Mary."

"You're right, but why are you doing that?'

"It is the only empty bed we have in ward-200. She needs to be in a room where she can get the best care we offer."

"Is that because she has more money than most of your patients?"

"No, it's because Emma and Shanika are on that ward. They are our best attendants and will provide the care Lizzy will need in her final days."

"My wife has lost three roommates. She has not gotten over losing Bertha yet."

"I'm sorry, but I don't have any choice right now."

"Yes, you do."

"What is it?"

"Give her Anna's bed and move Anna into our room. I promised her daughter I would look after her. I can do that if she is in the room with Mary."

The next day, Mary's new roommate moved in. She came carrying a harmonica.

❄

ANNA WAS UNHAPPY ABOUT MOVING FROM A ROOM she had known as home for four years. And when she was unhappy, she leaned on Papa to resolve her problems.

"Why are they taking my bed, Papa?"

"They aren't taking your bed. They are moving it to another room, where you will be with Mary and me. I will make sure they bring your mattress and pillow. How does that sound?"

"I don't like it."

"You will, I promise."

She glared at me as if she did not believe a word I was saying.

"You can play your harmonica any time you like. How about that?"

I could see she was considering my proposition, but she said nothing more. I pulled a chair from alongside the bed the aides were preparing and allowed Anna to sit. I took some grapes and cheese from Mary's refrigerator.

"Want some?"

She held out her hand for the paper plate I was already filling with snacks.

"I'll stay," she said, "but you have to leave the room when I am getting undressed."

"We have a deal, Anna."

I handed her the plate.

Chapter Forty-Three

THE BEGINNING OF THE END

We celebrated Anna's 103rd birthday without fanfare. I bought a small cake, which we shared with our favorite aides. Marie and Frank arrived early that Thursday morning and celebrated in the room with us. While Frank made his rounds as pastor to other patients, Anna and Marie sang the hymns they loved so much. I pushed Mary outside to enjoy the late summer weather, knowing that we would experience the chilly fall season in a few weeks.

Before Marie and Frank departed, I met them in the patient lounge, where Anna spent so much time watching the goldfish.

"I am concerned that Mother's condition is deteriorating," Marie said. "I notice she has lost weight since I was here three months ago."

"I thought she might have lost a few pounds, but, as you know, these people aren't permitted to reveal Anna's medical condition to anyone but her guardian," I said.

"Her memory is also worse. For the first time since I've been coming here, she couldn't remember the words to "It is Well with My Soul," and that is one of her favorite songs."

"I know. She plays it on her harmonica."

"She didn't want to play for us today," Frank said, "Does she still play very often?'

"Not as much as she used to," I said, "but when she plays, she still remembers to end with "Pop Goes the Weasel."

We all laughed, but only for a moment before the reality of what was happening to our loved ones returned to the moment.

"I see the same thing happening with Mary," I said. "Her lapses occur more often and last longer. Sometimes, she does not recognize me for the entire day."

Marie took my hand. "Thank you for looking after Mother. I know she can be a little cantankerous, but no one has a bigger heart than she does. If she knew how to express her gratitude, I know she would."

"I love that little lady, and it will break my heart when she has to leave us."

"I know," Marie said.

The thought occurred to me that Marie should know about her mother's favorite fish. I looked toward the fish tank. "Do you know George?"

"Believe it or not, Mother did tell me about him. Because he is always so gentle toward the other fish, she named him after my father. Which one is he?"

When I looked into the aquarium, George was floating upside down. I knew he was no longer alive. I could not bring myself to tell Marie the truth. A larger fish swam by. I thought of telling Marie the larger fish was George, but instead, I pointed at the fish floating upside down.

"That's George," I said.

"What do you think happened to him?" Marie stood on her tiptoes to get a better look at the dead fish.

"He probably died of a broken heart because Anna couldn't come to see him very often."

"Sounds like my father, for sure."

We watched the activity in the aquarium for a while longer.

Frank stood and asked us to join hands as he prayed: "Dear Lord, bless this place and all the patients and caretakers. Keep them in your grace. Especially bless our dear Anna and Mary as they face a dark abyss. How we hate to lose our loved ones before their time to the dreaded scourge of Alzheimer's. Even so, we take solace in knowing this is the path that will lead them to Heaven's gate. We know you will take all of us in your good time. We know not the day or hour when you will come for Anna and Mary or for us. Make the last days you choose to give them as comfortable as possible. For we who love them, continue to bless us as we travel and try our best to do works pleasing to you. We ask this in the name of your wonderful Son, Jesus. Amen."

THINGS WERE MUCH QUIETER IN THE ROOM WITHOUT Bertha. Before long, Mary, Anna, and I settled into a routine that was considerate of both of them. Anna played her harmonica infrequently. I am sure Mary loved the music when

Anna played. Anna still sang her songs of salvation but sometimes mixed the lyrics of one song with another. She took long naps during the day and ate very little of the food brought to her on a tray. I often chastised her for not eating, but my nagging didn't improve her eating habits. She usually resorted to her frequent retort to me: "When you get to a hundred, you can tell me what to do."

Mary was thirty years younger, but her health and memory seemed to deteriorate as rapidly as Anna's. The frequency of their lapses from reality increased as fall waned, turning into the normal southern Michigan early winters. To make matters worse, Shanika and Emma left Westwood for employment in a new facility paying higher wages. I had no idea how difficult my tasks of caring for the two women in my life would become without the aides I trusted and depended on so much.

Mary and Anna had meals in their room. Both required assistance opening milk cartons, removing cups' lids, and inserting straws into drink containers. None of this required explaining to Shanika or Emma, but the new aides, who often worked only a few days before being terminated, did not appear to comprehend such needs. Unless I was in the room at mealtimes, food trays would be left on tables beside Anna's and Mary's beds, with many items on the tray untouched. I recalled Mary's early days at the facility when I took issue with the staff and management on many occasions because of the quality of service being provided to her. Now, it looked as if I was back at square one just when my wife and her roommate needed the best care possible.

No one understood the difficulty of the jobs of the aides better than I did. I recalled working my way up from the shop floor to upper management of my small company, providing parts to General Motors, Ford, Chrysler, and independent automobile manufacturers. But I also recalled that whatever task was given to me, I did my best to do the job correctly. I expected no less from the attendants now charged with caring for Mary and Anna.

My requests to the aides turned into demands. When they went unheeded, I turned to the management. I went to the director's office. His secretary said he was busy taking phone calls from corporate. "Can you come back later, Jim?"

"No," I said. "I'll wait."

Twenty minutes later, Rob Donovan opened his door. "You want to see me, Jim."

"Yes, I sure do." Rob and I had frequent conversations, which usually resulted in favorable resolutions. I was confident he anticipated my reason for being there before we began our discussions.

"Come on in."

As I sat down, he said. "I know what you're here to hop my ass about."

"Maybe you do, Rob, but I want you to know the care your new aides are providing is piss poor."

"I know. It's like that all over my facility. I am losing my good people right and left because I can't pay them what our competition does. I was just on the phone with the president of the company, telling him we have to pay our employees better."

"What are they going to do about it?"

"A group from corporate is coming in this week to see what we need to do. There will be raises for our employees."

"Thanks, Rob," I said. "I don't wish to make problems for

you, but I want to know that if my wife and Anna Gamble have to die in this place, they will die with dignity. I appreciate whatever you can do to make certain that happens."

The following week, there were three new aides on ward-200.

Chapter Forty-Four

ANNA'S BLESSING

S pring came with no let-up in the demands for time and energy to cope with the pending demise of the two most important people in my life. Each morning when I arrived to see a hearse at the side entrance of the facility, I expected the body under the white sheet to be that of Mary or Anna. And, if, by chance, one of them was alert enough to recognize me when I got to their room, that made my day a success.

At the beginning of summer, Mary regained strength enough to request that I open her curtains. A few days each week, she wanted the television turned on for one of the inane game shows she used to enjoy. Inevitably, she fell asleep soon after she began watching, and I did not have the heart to turn off the TV until I left for the evening.

Anna was sleeping more and more and ignoring the food tray brought three times daily to her bedside. The aides did not seem to comprehend that she was too incapacitated to feed herself. I prompted her to drink water or milk without much success. She still asked for a Snickers bar when she was coherent, and I always kept one handy for her.

Marie and Frank visited twice during those days, but mother and daughter did not sing their hymns. Marie sat quietly by her mother's bedside while Frank made his usual rounds throughout the convalescent facility. The futility in Marie's voice told me her mother would not survive until her next birthday in August, but as usual, she defied the odds. Anna turned one hundred-four with me alone by her bedside, singing "Happy Birthday." We had no cake to share with the attendants. I gave her a Snickers bar with one small candle on top.

As I watched over her the next day, she reached under her pillow and handed me her harmonica.

"I couldn't," I said and attempted to give back the harmonica. She refused to take it, pushing my hand away. She closed her eyes, and shortly afterward, she slept.

Marie and Frank did not visit again until October. They kept abreast of Anna's condition by talking with the administrator or facility physician at least once each week, and I called Marie to keep her aware of things from my perspective. Frank's duties as a hospice pastor made him too busy to make the trip to Ypsilanti. I believed they knew Anna was in good hands while in the same room as Mary.

Frank returned from his rounds and said a short prayer at Anna's bedside. Before they left the room, he stopped by Mary's bed to pray silently.

Next morning, after the breakfast trays were picked up by the aides, I was surprised to hear Anna call my name, "Papa."

I walked toward her bed. "Yes, Anna."

"Papa," she said again.

I realized she was calling for her father, not for me. I sat next to her bed and took her hand in mine. Her frail voice said, "The Lord is my shepherd; I shall not want."

I waited to hear the remainder of the Twenty-Third Psalm, but she said nothing more. The only thing that came to my mind was "This Train is Bound for Glory.". I vowed then to learn to play Anna's harmonica.

I CHOOSE MY HEROES CAREFULLY AND FOR REASONS that are not important to some people. My heroes do not cross unknown oceans, invent medical cures, or walk on the moon. They have human frailties and desires. My heroes have more failures than successes. The one common trait of my heroes is perseverance—getting up after being knocked down, keeping faith in themselves, and fearing nothing but their own inclination to stop trying. That was the predominant trait of Anna Marie Gamble, shored up by an unshakable faith in God and her assurance of resurrection through Jesus Christ. How else could such a sickly, unwanted child survive unfathomable cruelties to make enduring contributions to her family, friends, and strangers, leaving all of us whom she touched to mourn her passing yet rejoice in the knowledge that if there is a Heaven, Anna is sitting on the right-hand side of God?

"Pop Goes the Weasel."

About the Author

Author, Lieutenant Commander Travis E Short, U.S. Navy retired, wrote his first book, *My Gun Cries Justice,* at the age of seventeen and published it in 2018 under the penname King Papa. Including *Anna,* he has published six books and is now publishing *The Adventures of Faraday Fox,* a book for young readers scheduled for release in the summer of 2023. A native of southwest Virginia, he grew up in the coal mining town of Jenkins, Kentucky, in the heart of the Appalachian coalfields. There, he gained an appreciation for the struggles and hardships of everyday Americans like him and his family. He drew on these experiences to bring Anna's story to light. Having joined U.S. Navy at age seventeen, he worked his way through the ranks and retired at age thirty-eight. He has a degree in Engineering Sciences from U.S. Navy Postgraduate School, Monterey, California. Before devoting his energies primarily to writing, he held ownership and management positions in the machinery manufacturing and shipbuilding industries. Mr. Short is the father of four daughters and three sons and now resides in Dahlonega, Georgia, and Moss Point, Mississippi, with his chief encourager, Shirley Adams.

For more about the author, you are invited to visit his website at TravisShort.com.

Acknowledgments

I must acknowledge Mr. Frank Eastland, CEO of Publish Authority, for his willingness to accept my book for review for possible publication. I am grateful to his wife, Bernadette, who encouraged Frank to publish *Anna*. The thought of turning my work over to the editor at Publish Authority sent tremors of fear to my heart. But any concerns I might have had were quickly dispelled when I began working with Nancy Laning. The book was made better because of her editing skills and sharp eye for details. And for that, I am grateful.

Most of all, I acknowledge Shirley Adams, whom I love, and whom I appreciate for her diligence in editing and re-editing the transcript until it was in a form presentable to the publisher.

Thank You for Reading

If you enjoyed *Anna,* we invite you to leave a review online and share your thoughts and reactions with friends and family.

Publish Authority